Mission of Love is mo

Roger Cole is a physicia

terminally ill. His story involves many people in the

last days of life. Yet such is the loving and spiritual nature

of his approach, these encounters brim with hope and

happiness. There is much about this book that will inspire

you. Above all, though, is the love that inspired it.

Paul Wilson, author of the calm book *series*

This is a generous and genuinely sustaining book.

It offers as much through its story of Roger Cole's own

profound spiritual development as through the many

compelling stories he tells. This is not a book 'about dying';

it's a book about the whole rich brew of existence,

of which dying is just a part.

Stephanie Dowrick, author of Forgiveness and Other Acts of Love

With a wise and compassionate heart borne of dedicated practice and study, Roger Cole presents us with a detailed understanding of the human condition and our spiritual capacities. His words liberate people from their fears and concerns as they realise their own potential for the experience of profound peace. Experiencing peace and equanimity in the midst of flux, change or catastrophe is the peace that passes all understanding. Using his extensive medical knowledge and experience combined with his spiritual understanding, Roger Cole sheds the light of wisdom upon our paths. Participants in our programs at the Quest for Life Centre find *Mission of Love* a source of easy-to-understand information that brings great comfort, insight and peace as it reminds them of their own creative potential.

Petrea King, Founder, Quest for Life Centre, Bundanoon

With humility and humour, Roger Cole beautifully shares a spiritual journey that will inspire and encourage many others to move towards a deeper understanding of life and death.

B. K. Jayanti, author of God's Healing Power
Europe Director, Brahma Kumaris World Spiritual University

As each of us faces death, what do we conclude really matters in life? *Mission of Love* wonderfully portrays insights from people who have been brave enough to share their answers from this journey. Reflecting on this wisdom, the rest of us can grow to lead richer, fuller lives. People's willingness to share their summations of life are a special encounter with the transcendent.

Professor David Currow, Head, Department of Palliative and Supportive Services, Flinders University, Adelaide

Mission of Love is a lovely book. Every minute I have I'm into it. I read the same chapter over and over again. There is so much spiritual wisdom in every paragraph … God bless Dr Cole and his work with suffering humanity.

Sr Mary Anthony of the Sisters of the Presentation of the Blessed Virgin Mary, County Kildare, Ireland

This is a book we have waited half a century to be written … It will bring joy, relief, hope and understanding to a great many lives. How I wish it had been available when first we heard that Damon, our youngest son, was going to die of AIDS.

Bryce Courtenay, author of April Fool's Day

Mission
of love

Dr Roger Cole, **MBBS, FRACP**, studied medicine at Guys and King's College hospitals in London from 1973 to 1979. He trained as a cancer specialist, and has worked as a palliative care physician from 1987. He is Director of Palliative Care for the Illawarra region of New South Wales. He has published articles on palliative medicine, grief, meditation and spirituality. From 1998 onwards he has extensively toured Australia, New Zealand, Asia, Europe and North and South America, giving public talks about meditation, inner healing, spirituality and the care of the dying. Roger lives in Wollongong with his son and daughter.

Mission
of love

*A Spiritual Guide to Living
and Dying Peacefully*

Dr Roger Cole

HACHETTE AUSTRALIA

HACHETTE AUSTRALIA

Published in Australia and New Zealand in 2008
by Hachette Australia
(An imprint of Hachette Livre Australia Pty Limited)
Level 17, 207 Kent Street, Sydney, NSW 2000
Website: www.hachette.com.au

Originally published by Thomas C. Lothian Pty Ltd 1999

National Library of Australia
Cataloguing-in-Publication data:

  Mission of Love / Cole, Roger

  9780733624117

  1. Self-realization. 2. Meditation. 3. Spiritual healing.
  4. Death – Psychological aspects. I. Title

  158.1

Cover photograph by Samantha Everton
Cover design by Michelle Mackintosh
Internal design and typesetting by Caz Brown
Printed in Australia by Griffin Press

Hachette Livre Australia's policy is to use papers
that are natural, renewable and recyclable products
and made from wood grown in sustainable forests.
The logging and manufacturing processes are expected
to conform to the environmental regulations
of the country of origin.

Foreword

It has always astonished me how many doctors turn out to be good writers, this especially, after looking at your average prescription one is forced to conclude that most medical practitioners must be verging on the illiterate.

It is perfectly valid to use the defence that content is more important than form, that what we have to say is more important than how we say it. Frankly, Roger Cole's book contains enough good material to make it valid if it had been written in mumble and grunt. But it isn't. It is delightfully written and lovingly told.

This is a book we have waited half a century to be written. That is ever since the medical profession became obsessed with pills and potions and forgot about love and caring. It will bring joy, relief, hope and understanding to a great many lives. How I wish it had been available when first we heard that Damon, our youngest son, was going to die of AIDS.

~

Roger Cole came into our lives when our son Damon was in the final stages of AIDS. He was born a haemophiliac and contracted the HIV virus from a blood transfusion in the very early days of the pandemic. At that time virtually nothing was known about the virus and, putting it into lay terms, the doctors, seemingly willy-nilly, threw everything at it, often with quite disastrous results.

To those readers who do not know the prognosis of AIDS, perhaps a short explanation? In a nutshell, the AIDS virus destroys the T-cells in our body. These are the cells which fight off infection, the infantry troops that prevent most of the deadly viruses and diseases, which lurk at the peripherals of everyone's life, from entering our bodies. In other words, they largely constitute our immune system. The AIDS virus eventually destroys all these T-cells allowing any number of diseases to invade the body without being repulsed.

The AIDS sufferer doesn't in a sense, die from a disease known as AIDS, but from a multiple number of infections which combine to kill him or her. At any stage he or she may be suffering with two or three different viral diseases, all of which require essentially different treatments using drugs which don't always work together. Add to this the fact that Damon was a haemophiliac which in itself required constant and complex medication and the result was that he was taking an unco-ordinated cocktail of drugs with disastrous effects.

One such drug would give him acute constipation which, in his weakened state, was severe enough to be life-threatening, the next would bring on diarrhoea which would leave him dangerously dehydrated, a third created acute nausea and yet another caused him to have severe fits. While it may seem curious in today's medical climate, with five different doctors caring for Damon at one time, none of them, to my knowledge, saw fit to check on the treatment each of the others had prescribed.

Damon was quite simply dying of the medication he was receiving and doing it real tough.

Then Roger Cole entered our lives. In my book *April Fool's Day*, there are two sentences which simply read: 'Dr Cole, if you read this book, please know how very much we are in your debt. Damon loved you and we thank you for your honesty, compassion and love.'

Roger Cole soon had Damon on a drug regimen that levelled out the peaks and the valleys, which made his life a great deal more comfortable. AIDS is an awful way to die, simply because you die of everything. All I can say is that, but for Roger Cole, my son would have died a terrible, terrible death. It isn't simply that he is a brilliant palliative care specialist, which he certainly is, but because as a man he returns the somewhat tarnished reputation of the medical profession back into a brilliance that makes him a wonderful exception, not only as a doctor, but as a human being.

~

Roger Cole, may your book sell a hundred thousand copies just for starters. It is a wonderful complement to your skill as a physician and will, I know, lead many a confused, desperate, weary and grieving family lost in a dark depression back into the pure light of understanding and hope.

Bryce Courtenay

Contents

Preface

I have been a doctor since 1979 and don't recall ever wanting to be anything else. I can't honestly say that compassion was my driving force. On the contrary, I was ambitious, motivated by self-interest and a fear of failure. I learnt nothing in my undergraduate studies to change this. I was trained to be scientific, clinically detached and uninvolved with human suffering. When I left university I had no idea that people need doctors who communicate and care. Actually, caring embarrassed me. It made me feel vulnerable.

In my final year as a medical student I did a six-week paediatric term in Darwin and fell in love with Australia. On an impulse I arranged to return to Darwin Hospital as an intern after passing my final examinations. My wife, Sue, had just graduated in dentistry and supported the adventure.

We had a wonderful year and Sue would have liked to stay, but I had other ambitions. I wanted to become a specialist physician, which meant a move to Sydney's Royal Prince Alfred Hospital (RPA). I thrived in the competitive, academic environment, which enabled me to remain goal-hungry, self-centred and successful.

At the end of 1983 my greatest moment came when I passed the physician's specialist examination. This enabled me to enter training in medical oncology (cancer medicine). With another three years of supervision I would become a Fellow of the Royal Australasian College of Physicians (FRACP).

After three months of euphoria I came back to earth. Having satisfied my highest aim there was nothing to strive for. I wasn't focused and I was burning out. There was a lack of discipline in my life and I had an identity crisis. Without a goal I felt empty and didn't know myself. I struggled and looked for new mountains to climb.

Fellow high achievers advised me to publish scientific papers, become involved in research and get a PhD to succeed in academic medicine. As I thought about this I discovered a new voice inside me. It was saying, *No. Consider others.* My ambitions had blinkered me into looking at sick people as problems to solve, rather than opportunities to help and to heal. I began to see beyond this arrogance. People were suffering and so were their families. I needed to understand this better and felt angry towards an establishment that seemed academic and out of touch. I started talking to my patients.

I explored what it was like to live with cancer, to face death and to lose someone you love. To my amazement it really helped them and I found people were appreciating me in a way I had never experienced before. They were teaching me compassion.

The turning point of my life was a workshop with Elisabeth Kübler-Ross in 1984. Its aim was to help professional people become more effective in caring for the dying. Its method was to have participants confront their own emotional pain. During the workshop I broke down and had a cathartic experience of grief followed by an intense feeling of pure, unconditional love, which I describe in Chapter 4. At that moment I felt separated from my physical body and experienced a blissful, unworldly happiness. For the first time in my life I realised that I was an eternal being and that love, peace and happiness were natural attributes of the soul.

I took the following year out of mainstream oncology to develop a centre at RPA to provide information, counselling and support for people with cancer. I learnt counselling techniques, developed cancer support groups and researched complementary therapies. I began to meditate and to teach meditation to interested cancer patients and their families. Above all, I let down my guard, developed a more open, easy nature and enjoyed being myself in therapeutic relationships. Having found love, I now discovered that healing is a balance between competency and compassion. Patients benefited most from my knowledge, skills and understanding when I was simply being human.

While developing as a physician I also started to integrate spiritual awareness into my work with people suffering from cancer, not by preaching but through the virtues of love and respect. I began to realise that we can reach people through our attitude and nature, and that spiritual development enables us to extend spiritual support without words. Though attracted to leaving medicine and following more esoteric healing practices, an inner voice told me I should stay in the orthodox system yet be eccentric to the 'mainstream'. I felt it had been no accident that a spiritual awakening had followed my specialist examination success. I was somehow meant to be where I was.

After completing my training in oncology I moved into palliative care, becoming the Director of Palliative Care at the Prince Henry and Prince of Wales hospitals in 1987. Providing comfort, support and relief for people who would die was very rewarding. It seemed such an honest expression of medicine and gave me a sense of serving humanity. There are remarkable lessons to be learnt from caring for people who are dying, especially when the state we call acceptance emerges. A soul is almost visible. Pure and peaceful, it can fill a room with love and leave everyone feeling that the 'death' was beautiful. Acceptance reveals an ever-present though forgotten potential of our souls — the ability to love unconditionally.

As I witnessed these things and began to speak of them, people were uplifted. It gave them a sense of their spirituality, a feeling of hope and a belief in love. I found a vocation in sharing observations and experiences. It has meant being, at times, both sincere and vulnerable. And at times taking risks within the establishment. This has been rewarding because I now feel love and regard for all those I work with and care for.

I have written *Mission of Love* in this vein. It is composed of stories from my spiritual journey, my study of meditation and my care of people who are dying. The aim of the book is to offer knowledge and insight, as well as a route to compassion and peace, in the hope that others will also seek understanding before the end of their lives. The book can best be considered a spiritual tapestry woven from people's lives, my own included. As spiritual evolution takes us far beyond everyday expression, I have had to search for the right words to express my deepest emotions, convictions and beliefs.

By drawing on personal experiences, and those of my patients, I have depicted spirituality as a process of enlightenment and self-discovery. Several meditation exercises guide readers through this process and its application to everyday life. Through this, I hope to engage our shared potential for change and growth.

Acknowledgements

In writing *Mission of Love* I am indebted to my patients and their carers. You have taught me to look deeper, to find love, to be less judgemental and to be more compassionate.

I have included many case studies in the text. For the majority, confidentiality has been maintained by writing composite stories or by altering details such as names, gender or diagnosis. In some instances identities are revealed or the stories are recognisable. I especially thank those of you who gave permission for their inclusion. You know who you are and I wish you to know that this has meant a great deal to me.

Mission of Love could not have been written without the wisdom of the Brahma Kumaris World Spiritual University. Many of the insights included within it reflect its teaching of

Raja Yoga Meditation. I would especially like to thank Baba, Dadi Janki and Didi Nirmala for their spiritual knowledge and guidance during the development of this book. Royalties from the sale of this book are dedicated to the worldwide service of this organisation.

I would also like to thank the people who read and commented on earlier drafts of this manuscript. I am especially grateful to Annette Robertson, Therese Nichols and Jo Heathcote in this regard.

Last but not least to Sue, Sam and Lucinda, my wholehearted love and gratitude for the time we have spent together.

Introduction

A nurse had left a message with my secretary about a young cancer patient who wanted to see me. I was very busy and the patient was already under another palliative care doctor. I rang the nurse and told her that I wouldn't be able to find the time, and asked if the patient could be reviewed by her own doctor. But the nurse was disarming and insistent.

'Only you will do, Dr Cole. She's read your books and has her heart set on meeting you before she dies. She wants to talk about spiritual things.'

I said that I'd see her in the morning.

Liz had been diagnosed eighteen months earlier with breast cancer. Despite all the chemotherapy it kept spreading and her condition deteriorated. Most recently it had gone to the lungs and her cancer specialist told her that nothing more could be done to contain it. She was stunned. *But I'm only forty-three*, she thought. Since then she had been at home with Don, her husband, receiving palliative care services from our team.

When I arrived at her house Don met me at the door. He beamed a huge, generous smile.

'Thanks for coming. She's like a child waiting for Santa Claus!'

I laughed and said that it was a pleasure. But I felt a slight disquiet. I wondered what she was expecting. I was a specialist physician and an author, an expert by all reports. Now I just felt exposed and ordinary, hoping that I wouldn't be a big disappointment. Don showed me to the bedroom.

What greeted me was breathtaking. Liz was sitting up in bed, the pillows strategically placed to support her weakened body. Her room was spotless and warmly decorated. Despite her physical appearance, Liz had a huge presence. Smiling like a delighted child, her eyes were bright and she looked as though she was in an aura of light. She was beautiful, happy and serene. I felt that I was with a very wise old soul. When our eyes met it felt familiar, as if we'd always known each other.

'It's so nice to meet you,' she said.

'And I'm happy to meet you,' I replied, settling into the chair by her bed.

I noticed a copy of the first edition of this book on her bedside table. It was all creased and dog-eared, and looked like it had been read a hundred times.

'I love your book. It's made all the difference. It's given me peace. I just wanted to tell you how much I appreciate you.'

I felt humbled, but humour came to my rescue and I picked up the book.

'Look what a mess you've made of it,' I said. 'It's falling apart. You've got sticky tape all over it!'

We both laughed at the sorry sight.

'Seriously, though, I'm surprised. My book deals with death and dying. Didn't you find the stories confronting?' I never imagined that people whose lives were threatened would read it.

'No,' she replied. 'I found them inspiring, and I read them as their stories, their testimonies. But I found myself in them. And when I was reading the book I felt my soul awakening into the presence of God. There were times when I felt I was floating, full of light and peace. I loved the story of the lady who realised that the wonders of nature were really inside her, and that all the beauty she had witnessed was her own.'

Liz looked at me. As our eyes met I was drawn into her serenity and peace. It felt as if we were dissolving into an invisible light. In a timeless moment I experienced union with her soul, and there was no feeling of separation between us.

'I can feel God now,' she whispered into the silence.

'Me too,' I whispered back.

Liz told me how much truth she had found and how deeply the meditation exercises had taken her into love and forgiveness.

'I lost all my fear when I realised that I can never die.

Everything about death is an illusion. Everything that is true is about eternal love. Nothing that is separate from love is real. You made me remember all these things. I have let go of all my grievances because they were separating me from love. I treasure this forgiveness because it has brought me peace.' Tears were running down her cheeks.

I took her hand. 'Liz, you are a living angel,' I said.

'I know,' she said, smiling. 'And that's the beauty of it. I know that it's true.'

~

Liz lived for a little while longer. Her husband described her dying as beautiful. He said that it was the most peaceful thing that he had ever experienced. Liz was a gift to me because she embodied everything that I have written about. She had become an example of my vision about who we are, under all the fear and conditioning of our lives. This book was not actually written for people with cancer, and I don't recommend it as a gift for people with life-threatening illnesses. It deals with death and dying, and they might find it confronting. It has, however, brought untold comfort to some who, like Liz, wished to explore their spiritual truths. You should read it first and decide for yourself before you give it to someone in these circumstances.

Many people who have cared for their loved ones through a terminal illness have found healing through this book. It has also helped many to feel comfortable around someone who is very ill. I have been told that anyone from any spiritual tradition can dip into this book and find some treasures. It is written for my fellow spiritual travellers. It's about love, compassion and caring, the things that are needed to bring peace into our world. Even the odd atheist has read it because its stories are full of our shared humanity. An atheist once told me that it had touched him deeply but that I 'lost the plot' here and there with the spiritual bits!

This is a book that has healed the lives of some people who were lost in grief, despair and hopelessness. They have told me that it showed them a light. I believe that that light was an awakening to the love that connects us all. It is a love that knows no limits and no boundaries. It is a love that liberates and frees us from everything that is unkind and meaningless, a love that ends all of our fears. This book is about such love. It is about you and me.

I

Dear John …

John had AIDS. This was in the mid-1980s before modern treatments were available.

Diagnosed four years earlier, he had fought to survive through orthodox and complementary medicine. His initial courage and optimism gave way to depression and hopelessness as he sensed failure and faced an inevitable decline. His partner and family would not let him give in and encouraged him to keep on fighting. 'With the right attitude, you can still beat it,' they told him. *God knows I've tried*, he thought.

By the time he was admitted for terminal care John's body was wasted and he was suffering. He was also totally dependent and aware that he was becoming demented. This misery was compounded by diarrhoea and incontinence. His carers were completely exhausted and had requested his admission.

John was only twenty-six and his family told me not to mention death to him.

When I met him it was evident that he would soon die. He appeared wretched and his body language begged me to go away. I could see it would serve no value to make him tell me his medical history; he needed gentleness, confidence and a sense of human kindness. But I could feel that he resented my intrusion and I was challenged about how to engage him.

'Does it hurt anywhere?' I asked.

'All over,' he replied. 'Look at me, what do you think!'

He was angry; I could feel his resentment. I was confused about how to go on.

'John, I will try to make you more comfortable, and do something about the diarrhoea,' I said. 'I have no idea what it is like to be where you are. I can see you have suffered terribly and I imagine that to be almost unbearable.'

'Almost!' he scoffed. 'Almost! I just can't stand it any more.'

'Help me understand it better,' I offered. 'What is so terrible for you now? What is it that you can't stand any more?' Reluctantly at first, but then with animation, he told me about losing his health and with it his dreams and aspirations. He described his physical distress, his black depressions, his anger at the 'incompetent' doctors who had failed to heal him. He described his loss of dignity. He told me how he hated counsellors and those who preyed on people like him. Then he went quiet and appeared to withdraw into himself. I decided to take a risk. Rightly or wrongly I asked him, 'Do you believe in any form of afterlife?'

He surfaced from within himself. Despite being exhausted, his eyes were fierce and their message was clear: *No bedside conversions.* His next words were angry, forceful and very final: 'When you're dead, you're dead. Finished!'

In the uncomfortable silence that followed, I felt I had blundered. I had hoped for a positive discussion that would have brought him some comfort. Instead, it seemed that I had ruined any chance of establishing a trusting relationship. But something occurred to me about the manner of his rejection. I realised that, having suffered for so long, eternal life to John meant eternal suffering. He could only project what he was now experiencing into the future. His hope lay in death because this represented an end to suffering. My introduction of the afterlife, though well-meaning, was a direct challenge to this.

I sensed that to give him hope I had to tell him he was dying, and that it would soon be over, even though his family had implored me not to.

'John, you are very near the end. I think there are only a few days remaining. We will make these comfortable for you. There is no need to fight any more. Your suffering will soon be over.'

There was a visible change in him. His eyes softened and filled with tears, the shadow of fear lifted. His anger dissolved and he uttered the last two words he ever said to me: 'Thank you.'

I sat with him as he relaxed, then left the room to see his family. Naturally, they were very angry with me for speaking to him of dying, but I helped them to understand that I had been sensitive and that it was now better for him to know.

Before John died the following day they had some special time together. Instead of imploring him to keep on fighting, they allowed John to die peacefully. In accepting his death, they supported him and let him go.

~

Before I met John I had already been on a spiritual path for some years. He taught me that spirituality is about sensitivity and responsiveness, rather than form and doctrine. Sensing that his principal need was freedom from suffering, I was able to give him hope. By finding a way to bring peace to his mind, I believe I served a spiritual need. By communicating this to his family, I helped them to let him go. In turn, this allowed him to die peacefully.

In writing this book I am indebted to John. He made me wonder. He made me wonder why some people have to suffer. He made me wonder why we become 'spiritually blind' and separated from our souls. He made me wonder what freedom from fear would be like; how it would be to experience the peace that was evident when he knew he was dying, and whether I would put it off until my own death to find out.

By making me wonder, he made me seek understanding.

2

Making a difference

When I first met Peter and Wendy they were in despair. Twenty-four hours later they had become happy and hopeful, which was remarkable, considering it was an outcome of palliative care. I never consider that palliative care is just for the dying. In fact, I introduce it as a problem-solving area of medicine.

'It's not about fixing the disease,' I tell my patients. 'It's about quality of life and helping you live with any problems that your illness can cause.'

When Peter arrived in my consultation room he and his wife immediately broke down and cried. They were very, very frightened. I let them settle, then asked them to take me through what had happened. Peter had undergone surgery to remove a cancer from his rectum ten months ago.

The diagnosis had been a great shock, but the post-operative news was everything they had hoped for. 'I got it all,' the surgeon proclaimed, and the couple celebrated their good fortune. However, recent blood tests were suspicious and led to a scan that showed incurable secondary cancers in the liver. This news was devastating.

'I thought I was cured,' said Peter. 'I'm so angry. My surgeon lied to me. How could he do that? Now he tells me that I've only got nine months. I'm fifty years old, my children are nearly grown up and life is good. I'm not ready to die.'

I let Peter ventilate his anger and frustration. As I listened to his worries and concerns I adjusted myself to his nature and developed a sense of how he dealt with life. It soon became apparent that he didn't really understand the disease or the situation. It was time to reframe this picture.

'You seem lost,' I said. 'Like being in limbo, scared and not knowing what to expect.'

'That's exactly how I feel. It's completely hopeless,' he said.

I began to inform him about his disease, emphasising some positive and hopeful aspects.

I explained how the primary cancer grew in the rectum, and how microscopic cells — undetectable at that stage — had travelled to the liver before the surgery. What the surgeon had told him was true as far as all the known disease was concerned. I said that although the cancer had now spread to the liver, there was no immediate threat to his life. He still appeared healthy and the liver was functioning well. I told him that a liver must lose more than seventy per cent of its capacity before the situation becomes life-threatening.

'It is only with time that we can be sure that the surgery has cured it,' I said. 'And there is no way of knowing about the cells growing in the liver before that. Your surgeon didn't lie to you, although he could have prepared you a bit better.'

As it had taken ten months for the secondary cancers to appear, I told Peter that his cancer might not behave too aggressively. I was hopeful that it would be slow-growing and said that the prognosis of about nine months was an average, meaning that many people live longer. I also told him that I had seen some people live for more than two years under such circumstances.

'You're not dying,' I reassured him, and I suggested that we should take 'stepping stones' into the future. 'We'll let time be our teacher. Sometimes doctors try to teach time, but they can only give you their opinion and they don't really know what will happen to you. There's no danger for you in the next three months. We can check things again then. If all is stable, then the next few months will be safe. We'll keep going along like this and if anything changes, we'll look at it then and work out the implications. We can cross our bridges when we come to them.'

As I spoke, Peter and Wendy looked as though a great weight had been taken off them. The information was accurate, and it put the present situation in the context of the past and future. They were able to let go of their anger towards the surgeon, and the shadow of death had been removed.

As Peter's fear began to recede, he asked me about death and dying. Once the immediacy of death becomes more distant, a patient often finds the courage to discuss it. Usually he or she states that it is the process, rather than death itself, which is the main fear. Pain, dependency on others, losing control and separation from loved ones are the things that distress people the most. As he talked to me about all of these things, Peter relaxed. He was relieved to share the burden. I was able to reassure him that pain could usually be controlled, and that very few people die in pain when there is good palliative care. I also told him that complete dependency is rarely protracted in patients with liver secondaries so he would not become bed-bound for months at the end of his life.

I finished the consultation by telling Peter and Wendy that I operate as part of a team. A nurse would visit the following morning and give them a phone contact for after-hours support. We had a social worker who could help them address practical concerns including financial problems, and who could offer counselling services to the family.

At the end of the consultation Peter and Wendy said that everything was much clearer and more hopeful. By understanding the disease and their circumstances they were better equipped to deal with the uncertainty of their lives. They could now look ahead and see that there was a future. They also felt supported. Speaking to me the following day, Wendy said that the nurse's visit had given her a feeling of security that she would not be alone.

~

Palliative care workers make a difference by knowing how to relieve suffering, by meeting information and communication needs, and by extending emotional, social and spiritual support. Through human interest and compassion, palliative care can help a patient move towards the deepest peace, love and understanding accessible to a human being. I am sure of this because of the times I have seen serenity emerge when someone reaches acceptance in the face of imminent death. We will now explore this state of acceptance and reflect on its spiritual implications.

3

Unfinished business

In the 1970s and 1980s, Elisabeth Kübler-Ross made a huge contribution to our understanding of death and dying. As well as writing her landmark book *On Death and Dying*,[1] this Swiss-born American psychiatrist travelled the world, passing on her ideas to health professionals. She taught that unconditional love and acceptance are to be found in all of us, but that unfinished business separates us from both of these.

Elisabeth identified that acceptance follows a struggle through shock, denial, anger, bargaining and depression, which are all normal reactions to dying. The beauty and peace of complete acceptance is not, however, the average way of leaving this world; many people die while still experiencing any, or all, of these adjustment reactions. While most find a measure of peace, it is 'unfinished business' that prevents them from reaching acceptance, although I believe that the process continues after death.

Unfinished business is the emotional 'baggage' that we carry from our past, and repressed grief is a major component. Its effect is best seen in the transformation that can follow the emotional outpouring of a catharsis. We will explore this over the next two chapters, and witness a spiritual potential that lies beyond pain, loss and negativity. This potential is accessible to all of us, but we must first realise that it exists.

In the early part of my palliative care career I routinely explored and confronted grief repression. The results were sometimes remarkable but occasionally damaging. I mention this to caution you about applying the approach that I used with Kristina, as the outcome is uncertain.

Kristina was a seventy-year-old Ukrainian widow. She was admitted to hospital for investigations, which revealed breast cancer with secondary spread to the liver. Although it was incurable, she was started on a hormone tablet to control the cancer. Kristina lived alone but had a supportive daughter, two grandchildren and a number of close friends.

Three months later she was readmitted with acute pain in her upper abdomen. Exquisite tenderness over a much larger liver indicated rapid progression of her disease. The pain was easily controlled using morphine and, as she refused to have any further anti-cancer treatment, I was consulted to advise on her continuing care.

Although Kristina's 'acceptance' and her ability to face death were admirable, I discovered these to be superficial. Applying a Christian philosophy of the Orthodox Church, she intellectualised that her dying would be 'at the ordained time'. She also described a 'close relationship' with her family and friends, yet wouldn't discuss her diagnosis with them. When interviewed separately, her daughter revealed that contrary to a close relationship, there had been longstanding ambivalence between them. Having never felt loved by her mother, she was now frustrated that Kristina was distancing herself even further. Kristina was discharged to the care of her local doctor, with my services available when needed. Neither Kristina nor her daughter felt that counselling would be helpful.

Two months later, I found that she had become yellow (jaundiced) from liver failure and was breathless due to fluid on her lung. Her daughter was very distressed, confiding that their poor relationship had continued to deteriorate. Her support had been rejected and, unable to embrace or express love for her mother, she felt helpless and inadequate. Kristina had avoided contact with friends and neighbours, isolating herself with an independence that alienated all the people she valued.

Kristina's willingness to discuss and accept death was again impressive. However, it was apparent to me that she avoided talking about separation or loss. Instead, she maintained the strong spiritual framework that safely intellectualised her dying. I decided to probe for grief repression with a question.

'Kristina, have you ever experienced any losses of your own, such as a death in the family?'

She hesitated and showed emotion for the first time during our interviews. With gentle prompting she told me of a road accident thirty-five years earlier, in which her six-year-old son had been critically injured. He had been admitted to hospital in a coma. Kristina maintained a bedside vigil but had had to leave the hospital for a short period. When she returned, she was shocked to find an empty room. During her short time away he had died.

At this point Kristina began to cry, telling me how she had been 'the strong one for the family', suppressing her grief while supporting everyone else. She related how much she regretted not being able to say goodbye to her child, how she had missed him all these years and how guilty she felt for allowing him to step onto the road. No further words were required or possible in the next quarter of an hour, as Kristina broke down and let go of the grief she had repressed for so many years. I sat with her the whole time until, gradually, her emotions lightened and she repeated over and over, 'It's better now, it's better now, it's better now.'

Following Kristina's death a month later, her daughter contacted me to express her gratitude. After the catharsis Kristina was loving towards her family, talked openly about her feelings and frequently embraced them. She apologised to her friends, disclosed that she was dying of cancer and finally developed the gentleness and peace of mind that characterise true acceptance.

Grief repression and its resolution affect adaptation to and acceptance of death. With repressed grief, people subconsciously avoid internal pain and sorrow by developing personality traits that counter this vulnerability. Kristina's early responses were self-protective. By intellectualising death she avoided feelings of separation and loss, while her fierce independence, self-isolation and rejection of family shielded her from becoming vulnerable through receiving sympathy and support.

By contrast, following a catharsis of grief and guilt, Kristina fully disclosed her situation and welcomed the support of her family. Beyond her 'unfinished business' we discover that acceptance is a peaceful, open state of mind and not simply an acknowledgement of death. There is deep spiritual significance to the peace that lies beneath the baggage of our lives, which is explored further in following chapters.

As I cautioned before, what I did with Kristina is not always beneficial. Nevertheless, when dying people mention past losses you have their trust and confidence, so by listening you can do them good. Let them cry if they need to. You are helping them towards acceptance.

4

Catharsis

I was ten years old when my sister died.

Elisabeth Kübler-Ross referred to unfinished business as an 'inner pool of pain' that is responsible for all of our negativity and mistrust. She believes that we first have to confront and let go of our own grief before we can effectively care for the dying.

In 1984 my life changed when I 'let go' and discovered the freedom that love brings. It began with Kübler-Ross on one of her Australian teaching tours. I attended a five-day Life–Death Transitional Workshop with ninety other people.

On arrival I was allocated a room to share with a stranger called Phil. I believe it was fate rather than coincidence that brought us together. He was a burnt-out hospital chaplain, an intensely compassionate soul who was fiercely angry towards the Catholic institution, which he perceived to be unsupportive, impersonal and dissociated from community needs. I was in a similar position, albeit in different circumstances. I, too, resented a system that seemed impersonal and uncaring.

At the beginning of the workshop we all assembled in the main auditorium, where we spent two hours introducing ourselves. The group, which mainly comprised health professionals, also contained psychotherapists, priests, lay people and a few cancer patients. In the second session we were each given a sheet of paper and a set of coloured crayons. Elisabeth asked us to do a drawing to depict our lives at that moment. When we had completed our drawings, Elisabeth selected two from the pile and asked a baffling question. 'Do these two people,' lifting first her right hand then her left for emphasis, 'need to be here?'

Remarkably, she was holding my drawing in her right hand and Phil's in her left. Elisabeth proceeded to discuss the significance of our drawings in relation to repressed feelings. She said that they bore striking similarities. Both were vigorously coloured in red, which signified anger, and generous measures of black, which intimated grief-repression or sorrow. Elisabeth said that our past, present, future and far-distant future are represented in the four quadrants of a page when we draw.

I was impressed by her interpretations and amazed by the coincidental selection of Phil's drawing; I was also happy. Out of a conglomeration of anger and grief, I had drawn a bridge in the top-left corner of the page — my far-distant future. Around the end of it was an abundance of purple, which indicated, we were told, that my life would culminate in spiritual growth.

The next session was very confronting. Elisabeth was sitting at the front of the room between two other facilitators. Before the three of them was a mattress with telephone directories neatly stacked at one end, and a pile of feather-down pillows at the other. On top of the directories was something resembling a truncheon. Viewing the scene I felt puzzled as Elisabeth instructed us to come forward if we needed to express any feelings. There was an expectant silence before a man came forward, knelt on the mattress and did something I was completely unprepared for. He screamed.

I recoiled in shock as Elisabeth placed a telephone directory in front of him, handed him the truncheon and told him to direct his anger. Beating the directory with the truncheon, he first hurled abuse at his father, then at anyone he perceived to have hurt him. Ultimately, he finished up in tears for the sorrows he had experienced in his lifetime.

This was the vein of the workshop for the next four and a half days. It was a Gestalt process, which brings out our most deeply repressed emotions. Ninety 'normal' people went on to share cathartic experiences in an atmosphere that felt increasingly supportive. Elisabeth encouraged us to come forward and express ourselves when someone or something made us feel vulnerable. Practically every conceivable trauma was covered: the death of loved ones, childhood deprivation, physical and sexual abuse, abortion, desertion, divorce, persecution, rape. It was an amazing education in how an individual can be influenced by an event of the distant past. Those who thought they had put 'it' behind them found their emotions reawakened with overwhelming force. It taught me how powerful repressive mechanisms are, that they can relegate such suffering to the subconscious and keep it in check.

I sat near the back of the room, feeling inhibited and wondering what I was doing there. As time went on I developed a growing immunity and became increasingly fascinated. What would it be like to be on the mattress? A few times over the coming days I endeavoured to go forward, only to be overcome by anxiety. On the fourth day Phil served as my cue, making his way to the mattress and venting his rage at the Church. My own feelings of anger surfaced and, as Phil finished, I rose and walked forward. I felt strangely dissociated, detached and isolated as I knelt on the mattress.

Like magic the truncheon appeared in my hand and a telephone directory opened in front of me. By the time I was finished, I had directed anger towards the medical establishment, my parents, my siblings and my wife — in fact, towards just about everybody who had ever loved me. Eventually, exhausted by the effort, I slumped, kneeling and defeated. And yet, I didn't feel any different. It seemed to have been a worthless catharsis.

Elisabeth then asked everyone to take a break, indicating that I should stay.

'It is not anger that you need to deal with,' she said when we were alone. 'It is grief.' Elisabeth's presence was all around me and, as she spoke, it felt as if I was being cocooned in love and light. I was aware of her looking not at me but *into* me, and it seemed as if she was connecting her very soul with mine. 'Tell me of your losses. Who has died that you were close to?'

The most recent death had been my grandmother. In the distant past there was also my sister Julie, who died a 'cot death' when I was ten. We spoke of my relationship with both of them and of my feelings when they died. Elisabeth handed me a soft pillow to represent them, prompting me to talk to them, to tell them how I felt. I did so, but it only seemed like 'going through the motions'. I wanted to cry but I couldn't. When it was apparent that I was stuck, Elisabeth's voice drifted in. 'There is a much deeper loss within you,' she said. 'Your greatest loss is not having unconditional love as a child. This is the deepest loss we all carry.'

The words were penetrating and affected me in an extra-ordinary way. I felt elevated, peaceful and blessed. A seed had been planted which germinated the following day, when one of the participants was grieving for a child killed in a boating accident. The little one's body had never been found, and the mother was reliving every vivid detail. As I sat in the middle of the room, I experienced a tearing emptiness inside me; the same hollow void that accompanied the knowledge that I would never see Julie again. Drawn into an abyss of guilt, shame and anguish, I rocked back and forth, hunched over, my face buried in my hands.

I regressed and was no longer a rational adult, blameless for his sister's death twenty years earlier. I became the child again, ten years old, with my sister suffocating in the next room. It was my fault. Overwhelmed and irrational, I experienced a choking feeling as my heart broke. The catharsis that followed had an intensity that was greater than any single bereavement; it went beyond the loss of Julie. Julie was to be, in fact, the instrument that released me from repression and sorrow. I was about to realise that Julie had planted a seed of love and awareness that had remained dormant all these years. It was as if she herself was responsible for my spiritual awakening.

Once my heart had broken, it seemed to empty of sorrow and to open up. It was then, when I was completely vulnerable, that an incredible feeling of love and peacefulness began to flow into me, during which I seemed to detach from my physical body. There appeared to be light all around me, and a deep silence suffused with pure, unconditional love. Time stood still. It was as though a divine presence was filling every part of my being with unlimited love, until I felt merged and indivisible from it. It was an all-unifying experience during which I was somehow lifted beyond the material confines of our world. Later, when I 'returned' to the room, the feeling of contentment was awesome and beautiful. For the rest of the workshop, and the next few weeks, I remained in this elevated state with a feeling of radiant love for every human soul and every manifestation of nature.

The catharsis had brought enlightenment. Letting go of sorrow allowed me to glimpse the soul, its hidden nature and qualities. I now reflect on this as a 'spiritual window' through which I discovered my true identity, purpose and destiny; it showed me what I could become. As pure love was revealed to me after I 'let go', I knew that the love had always been present, though hidden beneath layers of *acquired* pain.

In the same vein, when someone lets go and enters the state of acceptance before dying, I believe that they experience unconditional love and happiness.

5

Acceptance

'My mother's peace was radiant and the room was filled with love.'

June was talking to me about the death of her mother, Margaret. When told that her ovarian cancer was incurable, Margaret was shocked and couldn't believe it. At first she thought that the doctors had made a mistake. Then, after realising it was true, she rejected the implication that she could die of it. As she deteriorated and this implication became real, she got angry at the world. 'Why me?' she cried. June was often on the receiving end of this anger, which was followed by tears of guilt and remorse. Fortunately, June was both loving and wise, and understood that her mother simply needed an outlet.

As Margaret became weaker, her anger gave way to depression and hopelessness. She began to grieve about the growing reality that she wouldn't be with her family for much longer. She had aimed to be around for her grandson's university graduation, but now accepted that this would not be possible. Gradually, as she began to yield and give up the struggle, she started to accept what she had been fighting against. She would talk to June about what she wanted at her funeral and who was to receive various possessions. To everyone's amazement, Margaret became happier and more contented as she faced her death. Instead of fearing it and struggling against its injustice, she let go and her suffering ended. She told June that 'dying is like a walk in the park'.

June told me that she and her sisters were all present when Margaret was dying. 'It was beautiful,' she said. 'Mum had a presence about her and a contentment that made everybody feel uplifted and happy. I will never forget the power of the love that emanated from her. It was really special.'

Here, June was describing her mother's state of acceptance. I enquired further: 'At the end, was she troubled by her looks and appearance, or about the disease and the fact that she was dying?'

June replied, 'No, mum was at peace with herself. Even though she was wasted, it was as if her body had ceased to exist. Only serenity remained and there was no fear in her at all.'

I next asked, 'Did your mother seem concerned or worried about any of you at that time?'

'No,' she replied. 'Mum knew we were there, but she seemed beyond any concern for how we were coping or feeling.'

'What about the problems of our world,' I asked. 'Was your mother affected by the deprivation and conflicts that are going on?'

June smiled, then said, 'Mum always had a strong position on everything and used to get really agitated about such things. But, now you mention it, no, she wasn't troubled at all. I guess she must have let go of everything.' June faltered for a moment, searching, then she repeated. 'She had let go of *everything!*'

Finally, I asked, 'After letting go, just before she died, did your mother seem burdened by any of the roles or responsibilities of her lifetime?'

'No,' she said. 'She had become free … *completely free!*'

∼

When someone is dying, it is a privilege to witness this state of acceptance. In her final days, Margaret became a free spirit, her soul naked and exposed before leaving the body. She was a gift to her family because she was revealing the truth of a spiritual identity that lies within. Through love and peace, the soul was 'visible' and accessible to anyone who cared to be with her. June told me that the experience left her with a firm conviction about eternal life. It was as if her mother had become a 'mirror', reflecting back the truth of the soul to those who visited her.

June's mother is living proof that real dignity lies within the soul. Once liberated, despite being physically wasted and completely dependent, she gained grace and revealed her inner beauty. Her soul was liberated when it no longer had any interest in the body and its appearance; when it was no longer worried about roles and responsibilities; when it had let go of relationships; and when it was detached from the problems of an increasingly complex world.

Once free from concern about her body, the world and relationships, Margaret entered a state of being in which she was completely *soul-conscious*. Her presence filled the room with a radiance of love that reflected, I believe, a return to what she had once been — *a peaceful soul*.

In Margaret's experience we see how one's spiritual identity can surface in the face of death. The question is, do we have to wait until death to find serenity? And must we be forced into submission before we can love and let go? I now believe it is possible to attain this liberation in life, and to rediscover our spiritual identity.

Let us now travel from one end of life to the other, where we will explore the quality of innocence and how it is 'lost' to the world we live in.

6

Innocence

In a national speaking tour around Australia, I asked audiences in every city to comment on what makes a newborn attractive. What is it about a baby, a puppy or a kitten that captures our hearts? The universal answer was *innocence*. Everybody also agreed that the quality of innocence embraces purity, openness, trust and vulnerability. When you think about it, we were all born like this. However, we knew nothing about the body or relationships and this inexperience rendered our innocence vulnerable. It is this ignorance, I believe, that leads us away from the soul's original nature of purity and peace.

One day, while sitting in a park, I was watching two children playing on the swings. Both were around two years old. When they got down, their mothers suggested that they hold hands. The little girl happily linked hands with the little boy, whereupon he immediately threw her to the ground. She was inconsolable, not from being physically hurt but from the shock. It had been totally unexpected. The boy was reprimanded as the girl was comforted. Then, when they were ready to leave, the boy's mother told him to hold her hand again, properly. He held out his hand to her.

She stepped away from him, withdrew her hands and put them behind her back. She had learnt fear. Having experienced betrayal, she was unwilling to trust and found it necessary to protect herself. She was not as innocent as she had been before the incident. Now more experienced, she would no longer be so unconditional and open with her trust. A small impression of doubt and uncertainty about relationships had been imprinted on her mind, and a small layer of defensiveness was now in her character. Although she had become less vulnerable, a tiny part of her inner beauty had been blemished.

Consider for a moment the vast challenges we face in our lives. Although we have many experiences of joy and happiness, how many undermining encounters have we had? All of us go through different forms of physical, mental or emotional pain at some time or another. Extrapolating from the little girl, it doesn't take long to realise that our original personality is modified by experience. As we layer ourselves with defences and withdraw our trust and openness, innocence is lost.

We are also conditioned to think of ourselves as physical beings, adopting an identity that reflects name and bodily form. To begin with, this identity is relatively simple, but in time it becomes more complex. Through it we learn to separate and discriminate on the basis of gender, familiar relationships, skin colour and culture. We develop a sense of individuality and, with it, desires to have or to possess for the self. As ego develops in this way, so the pursuit of self-gratification makes us increasingly dependent and creates expanding needs. We also become more fearful due to the potential for loss or deprivation when our desires go unfulfilled.

A child can be happy for no reason. In time, however, happiness becomes dependent on fulfilling desires. We forget the love that is intrinsic to the soul and begin to seek it on the outside. Eventually, our ability to experience peace, happiness and love is surrendered to the stability of external circumstances and relationships.

At birth our state of being can be referred to as *soul-consciousness*; it is innocent yet ignorant of the world. In time, the soul is deceived as it develops *body-consciousness* and ego. When this happens we become dependent on health, wealth, status and relationships to feel loved, valued and secure. As these are subject to change and fluctuation, so too are our peace and happiness, and our contentment comes under constant threat.

To ward off insecurity we develop negative attributes such as greed, possessiveness and anger, which either sustain us or make us feel more in control of our world. However, when they fail us and we lose control of our circumstances, we can become anxious, stressed, desperate or depressed.

All this represents body-consciousness, which is like a veil shrouding the true and original identity of a soul. Yet the peace, love and purity, and the openness, trust and innocence of our original nature (our soul-consciousness) has not been lost. It is the hidden truth that lies within — a truth we see revealed once again when a soul is returned to love in the state of acceptance.

It is, I believe, this 'veil' of body-consciousness that Kübler-Ross identified as unfinished business. And it is behind this veil that purity hides. I am fortunate that she had this insight and showed health professionals a way to discover their truth. My experience of soul-consciousness followed a catharsis, proving to me that our innocence is preserved and can re-emerge. When this happens in life it is experienced as enlightenment, which, paradoxically, means only to rediscover who we were.

To grow spiritually we need to let go of our conditioning and break down our body-consciousness. While we can learn from acceptance, there is surely a better way than dying to renew our innocence. I would suggest adopting a spiritual life that allows us to develop self-awareness while relating to a higher power.

It would also be helpful to have some more objective evidence for a spiritual dimension, including an afterlife.

7

Afterlife

I often ask patients if they have any philosophy or beliefs about what happens after we die. Not infrequently they smile and say, 'Nobody has ever come back to tell us, have they?' I think they're mistaken. In fact, I believe that contact is frequently made by souls after they have left the body. There is a huge body of literature about metaphysical and paranormal phenomena, ranging from out-of-body experiences to apparitions and 'miracles'. Nevertheless, as this is all anecdotal and doesn't prove the existence of the soul, most people remain sceptical. Minds only open after significant and validating spiritual experiences.

Studies have confirmed the frequent occurrence of paranormal experiences across many cultures. Random sampling of the general population in countries that included the

United States, Great Britain, Germany, Italy and Iceland concluded that more than a quarter of subjects had had a paranormal experience.

One striking anecdotal report appeared in the *Lancet* medical journal. A neurosurgeon, who describes himself as pragmatic, recounts the following experience:

> When I opened the kitchen door all appeared normal but then there seemed to be a curious descending dark shimmer in the far part of the kitchen, immediately gone but I knew it was death and female ... As I reached the bedroom, the doorbell rang and I was not surprised to see the village policeman who said he would be grateful for my help.[2]

The doctor then explains how the policeman had been on his way to tell his neighbour that her sister was seriously ill. Just as the policeman arrived he received a radio message that the woman had died. Knowing that the doctor lived next door he called to seek help in dealing with this sensitive matter. The doctor concluded: 'There was a message in my mind. How it reached there is not defined. Although first confused with fear, it was so very clear.'

A survey conducted by Dr Michael Barbato in Sydney documents paranormal experiences in relatives after their next of kin had died. It shows that paranormal phenomena, such as a vision of the person who died, occurred in at least eighteen per cent of cases. A patient's daughter related one such instance to me. Although her father was jaundiced and wasted, she told me how wonderful it was to be present at his death. She said that she 'saw' his soul leaving the body. It was only momentary but there was an instant where she witnessed his passage. Her mother, on the other hand, was haunted by the memory of his physical appearance, and her grief was intense for the first two months. Then one night he appeared to her, standing at the foot of her bed, smiling and in full health. Although he didn't try to communicate, she felt warm, peaceful and happy. By the time he disappeared, he had deleted the image of his dying body from her mind and left her knowing that she would see him again one day. The intensity of her grief diminished overnight.

It is also common for someone close to death to have visions of relatives who have already died. Sometimes when I'm sitting by a patient's bed, I notice the person looking at or talking to someone who 'isn't there'. One lady who had been unconscious suddenly sat up, looked at an empty chair in the corner and said, 'Oh, it's you,' then lapsed back into a coma. I believe that spirits are sometimes attracted to visit and comfort the dying during the terminal phase. A relatively frequent occurrence is the apparition of a child.

On one such occasion a forty-year-old patient and her husband had been independently seeing the apparition of a little girl. It began in the last three to four months of Joy's life with multiple myeloma, a cancer of the bone marrow.

'She used to come and look in through the window,' Joy told me. 'She was very pretty, about six years of age and always had a smiling face. When I went to the window and looked out there was no one there. One day I noticed David staring at her too and I said: "You can see her too, can't you?"'

It turned out that David had been seeing her the whole time, but neither of them had told the other. They hadn't wanted to alarm each other. It became a very comforting experience for them and it proved to both of them that there was an afterlife. How can two people independently have the same hallucination? Clearly, the child was real and spiritual.

For me, existence of the afterlife was confirmed by one significant experience. Trudy came to see me with her husband, Jim, who was in his mid-forties with advanced bowel cancer. He was wasted and terminally ill. Troubled by recurrent bowel obstructions and painful pelvic disease, Jim was depressed by his condition, while Trudy was a dedicated carer whose love, commitment and tolerance knew no boundaries. She was also a registered nurse working in the operating theatres of a local district hospital.

Jim was dealing with his situation in a somewhat intellectual manner. He carefully guarded his feelings and avoided vulnerability. He did, however, fully acknowledge his disease and the implications of it being incurable. With this understanding and his strong intellect, Jim was a fighter who would never give in. Wanting to live for as long as possible, there was no way he was going to lie down and die.

Jim, Trudy and I were sitting in an outpatient consultation room. We had spent some time going over recent problems and I had just outlined a new management plan to address these. At that point I asked Jim how he had been coping mentally, expecting him to say, 'Fine, no problems.' To my surprise he opened up for the first time, saying that he was upset about his adolescent children. Knowing that he wouldn't be around in the future, Jim was driving their maturation. He was trying to fulfil in months a role that he might have played over the next ten years. Being in their early teens, however, the children were at a stage of development where they could accept parental support and guidance but not direction. Conflict arose as they refused to allow Jim to direct their lives and future career options. He became very depressed about it.

While I was listening to Jim's story, I began to experience a very deep and empathic bond to him. In fact, I was so engaged by him that the world around seemed silent and distant. As I took my turn to speak, Trudy seemed remote and only on the fringe of my awareness. I pointed out the problems I saw in Jim's endeavours. Though understandable, it was placing his children under too much pressure, and it would be better to ease back a little. I went on to say how I felt he would fulfil their needs in the future.

'Jim, when someone dies while we are still young, he or she leaves behind a "seed", which germinates in its own time. I once had a sister who died when I was ten. She left in me a potential that I realised twenty years later.' I went on to relate some of the Kübler-Ross experience covered in Chapter 4, then concluded: 'Julie died, but the seed she left behind eventually led to my enlightenment. It was a gift far greater than she could have managed if she had lived. She became, in effect, my guide and teacher in later life. Likewise, Jim, give your children love and a relationship free from expectations. In this way, you will accompany them through their lives and give them more than your physical guidance ever could.'

While I was speaking there was a sensation of love and peace connecting and surrounding us. I had only a distant sense of my own body and felt an exquisite lightness of spirit. It seemed as if a silent, powerful, healing presence was with us.

After the consultation I was given a message from Trudy, asking me to contact her. She wanted to speak to me about something that had happened during our meeting. Trudy was nervous when I called. She seemed to be sounding me out to see if I would give her the space to say what she needed to. I prompted her, but nothing could have prepared me for what she said or the dilemma it would create.

'When you started sharing your experiences with Jim, a little girl came into the room,' she said. 'She was quite beautiful, about seven years old. She danced around you the whole time and it seemed that you had a special connection with her. She was happy to be close to you and really joyful that I could see her. She told me that she wants you to tell her parents that she is happy and dancing again. Who could she be?'

I was too surprised to consider the question immediately, so I asked one of my own.

'What did she look like and where is she now?'

Trudy described her, giving special attention to a unique

curl in her hair, which dipped over her forehead. I couldn't think of anyone matching the description. As for where she was now, Trudy said 'Right here with me. She stayed with me and won't leave until I have done what she wants.'

'Has this sort of thing happened before,' I asked her, 'and can't you ask her who she is?'

'Yes, it happens from time to time. When a spirit comes, it stays with me until I satisfy its wishes or refuse to comply. I comply unless it is malevolent, in which case I turn my back to make it go away. They don't actually speak in words, but my understanding couldn't be any clearer if they did. I can't speak to them, so it's not possible for me to ask questions. It always ends up being a bit of a puzzle like this, I'm afraid.'

'Why didn't you tell me earlier?' I asked.

'I didn't know how you'd react. You don't just come out and say things like this to a doctor, so I thought it safer to tell your secretary first. She told me there was a girl of around this age under your care a year ago.'

I cast my mind back and remembered the child in question. 'Yes, little Tegan Sowry. But she bore no resemblance to the description you just gave me.'

'It's her,' Trudy exclaimed.

'How can you say that?' I asked.

Trudy was laughing on the other end of the phone. 'Because,' she replied, 'when you said her name, she jumped up and down, clapping her hands. She's so happy now.'

I considered this and then asked, 'So what am I supposed to do now?'

'Ring her mother,' Trudy replied.

'You're kidding,' I protested. 'I can't do that. I've no idea what's happened there since Tegan died. And I don't even know for sure it's her.'

'Just ring her and see,' said Trudy, clearly amused by my confusion.

After hanging up I thought about Tegan. I only visited her once, towards the end of her illness. After that I stayed in touch with her mother and the family doctor by phone. Tegan had a degenerative neurological condition that had affected her from the age of four. She gradually lost mobility and the capacity to communicate. When I saw her she was seven and couldn't walk, talk or do anything for herself. She was chair-bound and completely dependent on her mother. There was nothing I could think of that resembled Trudy's description.

I also had another dilemma. How would her mother react to me telling her this story? I had no idea what problems it might cause the family. They might not believe it and I had no way of knowing whether it would cause further distress. On the other hand, I had had a good rapport with Beth, Tegan's mother, and I remembered that she had a strong spiritual side to her. On these two counts, I felt that it would do no harm to at least contact her.

I phoned her to arrange a meeting. She was happy to hear from me but wary, and couldn't understand why I wanted to meet her. Rather awkwardly, I decided to discuss it with her over the phone. I said that Tegan had made contact with me, through a nurse who was psychic. I went on to describe what had happened. Beth interrupted me briefly. 'Tegan loved to dance before she got too sick.' As I was giving her the description, Beth exclaimed, 'I always used to do her hair that way, with a little curl over her forehead! It made her look so sweet.'

By this stage I started to get goosebumps. At the point where the little girl jumped up and down clapping, Beth just said, 'Oh, my dear God. That's exactly what she used to do when she was happy or excited. It's definitely her. I've just got goosebumps all over.'

'Me too,' I said, relieved now that her identity was clear. 'Tegan asked me to give you a message. She wants you to know that she is happy and dancing again. You don't have to feel sad any more.'

Beth wanted to speak to Trudy, so I gave her the contact number. They spoke together and were able to confirm Tegan's identity with an old photograph. Tegan herself took leave of Trudy when I was speaking to her mother. She has never tried to make contact again.

As for Jim, he defied all expectations and lived for another year. By letting go of his need to be a 'good father', he actually succeeded in this endeavour. Trudy and I still have contact with one another, in the bond that was tied by Tegan.

Tegan demonstrates a potential beyond all physical limitations. She appeared to Trudy in a non-physical form of light. Within this her psyche was intact and her individuality maintained. She was also still attached to her family and had the desire to relieve her mother's grief.

There are two things that validated Tegan's apparition, and demonstrated that death is but a separation of 'the self' and the body. Neither Trudy nor I could identify the child who presented features and mannerisms that were only known to her mother. When I had visited Tegan she had been paralysed and bed-bound. Even if I had seen an old photograph there was no way I could have known these mannerisms. There is no doubt that Tegan was real.

She is also evidence that we are more than a physical body. She appeared in an ethereal form of light with the identity of her recent life. Not only do we exist after death but we also maintain our identity. As she left the physical body in her ethereal form, it stands to reason that these are superimposed during 'life' and separate at 'death'. It is quite possible that the 'light' people experience in 'out-of-body' and near-death experiences is their own ethereal form. It is also quite possible that we can learn to experience our light form through meditation and other spiritual practices.

I am now certain that there is life after death, and that there is purpose, reason or meaning behind everything I witness or experience. In fact, I no longer believe in death as a reality. If we open our minds and listen with our souls then we will realise that mortality is an illusion we project from our limited perception.

8

Enlightenment

Spirituality is relatively unimportant to most people's lives. The experience of enlightenment can change this, as there is no turning away from the spiritual insight it brings. It is best considered a gift, substantiating an existence that is not confined to the physical plane.

The two main features of enlightenment are *experience* and *recognition* — the experience of love, peace and purity, and the recognition that these are qualities of the soul or of a higher power.

A few years ago I saw Joe, a truck driver who was married and in his mid-fifties. A local doctor requested a home visit, as Joe was in too much pain to come to the hospital. He lived several kilometres from any main roads. I arrived at the homestead, which was set in natural rainforest, on a cool spring morning. Closing the car door, I was enveloped by complete silence as I stood in the tidy, well-kept garden.

The serenity and beauty of the garden was a striking contrast to the atmosphere within the household. When his wife, Anne, opened the door, her sunken face, furrowed brow and the dark shadows around her eyes revealed her exhaustion. She was at the end of her tether.

Lying on the lounge, Joe was calm enough until he moved to greet me. The effort brought on a severe spasm of pain in his buttocks and legs. He exhaled sharply and carefully settled himself back into a more comfortable position. I administered a morphine injection for pain control, then explained my role and why I had been asked to see him. Joe relaxed, indicating that the morphine was taking effect.

He had had a successful operation for bladder cancer three years earlier, but relapsed two years later with secondary cancer in the spine. Radiotherapy provided relief at first, but the cancer spread progressively to involve more of the bones in his lower back and pelvis. In the last two months he had experienced increasingly severe chronic pain, only partially relieved by further radiotherapy. Despite oral morphine, the pain became almost incapacitating when he moved. Worse still, he became breathless — an X-ray revealed secondary cancers in his lungs. Joe would not live very much longer.

After reviewing his medications, I was confident I could improve the situation to give him much greater freedom of movement, with the prospect of a better quality of life. Joe was encouraged, relieved by the idea that he would not have to keep on suffering to the end. I asked him how he viewed his current circumstances.

He immediately volunteered that he couldn't see himself living much longer. Joe was keen to discuss the subject of dying, which everyone, to his frustration, had been avoiding. I asked him how he felt about dying. He said he was not afraid, especially now he understood that the pain could be controlled. I then asked if he had any particular beliefs or philosophy that had made the idea more comfortable to him.

As he hesitated and I waited, the room seemed to become still and peaceful around us. Joe told me there had been an experience that he had never shared with anyone because he had thought no one would believe him, and had worried about appearing foolish. With genuine interest I prompted him to tell me about it. When he was thirty-two, Joe told me, he had had an operation to repair a simple hernia in his left groin. In the post-operative recovery room he had had a cardiac arrest and 'died'. He felt himself float out of his body towards the ceiling. There followed an extraordinary sensation of serenity, as he was surrounded in golden-white light. He felt blissful, free and liberated, yet alert and fully aware, without any bodily sensations.

Down below he observed resuscitation attempts on his physical body, while up above he could see a swirling light that appeared to be beckoning. For just a moment there seemed a choice, which ended abruptly as he was shocked back into the physical, searing pain in his chest and struggling to breathe. Yet, strangely, he felt detached, with no fear of death despite the unpleasant sensations and effects of resuscitation. He had never feared death from that day on.

For Joe, this experience established beyond doubt the existence of a spiritual dimension. His nature changed considerably as a consequence. Joe became less of a perfectionist, more at ease and more tolerant. He said that others found him to be more dependable and stable in comparison with his pre-operative personality. Up to the day of my visit, he had kept all this to himself, fearing derision, rejection or mockery. Now, in the face of death, sharing the experience left him joyful, as he again tasted the reality of his soul. Joe had described both the experience and the recognition that characterise enlightenment. He was aware that he was eternal and that the change in him was clearly visible to others. Afraid of rejection, however, he didn't explore the experience or its implications any further.

This keeps the potential within enlightenment dormant, whereas deeper recognition of its spiritual implications and a willingness to change oneself leads to the path of *realisation*. This path is also accessible to anyone who has spiritual insight and the desire to reach their full potential.

9

The path of realisation

To 'recognise' means 'to know again' or 'to identify as known before'. It is very easy to apply this to something physical, such as a possession or an old friend. What is more challenging, yet just as relevant, is to apply recognition to one's 'inner self'. In the preceding chapters I have encouraged you to think of spiritual identity as something that is modified by life experience. I truly believe that we 'forget' who we are in the course of our lives.

When there is enlightenment, one is really recognising ('knowing again' or 'identifying as known before') the true and original nature of the soul. Recognition implies that this is nothing new and that spiritual growth is a paradoxical process in which we return to our original nature. To 'realise' means 'to make real' or 'to bring into fact'. As we realise our spiritual identity, it is 'made real' and becomes apparent. When thought of in these terms we begin to see an enticing possibility — that truth resides within us and that its realisation reveals our spiritual identity.

The journey or path of realisation is one of inner healing and renewal, which enables us to be open and loving, without vulnerability or dependency. It could be viewed as a journey in which we return to a pure form and expression of love that is both unconditional and spiritual. The path of realisation, whether through faith or enlightenment, requires both spiritual awareness and personal endeavour. We need to make an effort to hold onto peace and spiritual values, while living in a world that constantly challenges these.

I believe this state of realisation to be more important than the belief systems or religions that we follow. Values inherent to love are the essence and common aim of all religions. Whether discovered through a particular spiritual path or on the basis of personal experience, such values express our spirituality. I also believe that everyone has a spiritual path, which remains latent until something awakens us to it. Hidden within each person is the original nature of the soul waiting to be experienced, recognised and realised.

Emotional pain, fear and repression separate us from experiencing this inherent beauty. If we can reverse the conditioning of our lives, then we can realise the truth that resides within us. The path of realisation is a journey within, to appreciate the intrinsic divinity of the soul.

I shall now be looking at the efforts required to transform

weaknesses that separate us from experiencing love, unity and peace. These will be seen as conditioned and habitual personality traits that were not part of our original nature. Because such traits are acquired through the mistaken identity of body-consciousness, they can be transformed through spiritual knowledge and awareness.

Appreciation

When I first met Margo she was fifty-three and had been diagnosed with breast cancer for four years. Although initially slow-growing, the disease had become more aggressive over the last year. Despite several courses of chemotherapy, it had spread to her liver and lungs. We discussed her illness, life and family, her aspirations and disappointments. She had divorced ten years earlier, retaining custody of her only daughter, Genaro. They were inseparable. Her greatest regret was leaving Genaro and not seeing her grandchildren grow up. She felt all right about dying but was distressed for her family. 'I can't bear to see them so upset about me,' she once confided.

Margo had spent a year of her adolescence living among indigenous North Americans. As a result, she became something of a spiritual eccentric in her adult life. With respect for the land and all its creatures, she believed her spirit would return to the earth, living on in the forest, in the wind and in the sea. She would visit her family and meet with elders of the spirit world. As her first love was nature, she wished to be cremated on an open woodpile in the forest.

When Margo was dying she needed assistance to walk, shower and go to the toilet. I had taken to visiting her at home rather than seeing her in the outpatient clinic. She lived in a house under a rocky escarpment in dense bushland with elevated sea-views. Genaro had moved in to look after her. When I called one November morning, Genaro's smiling face greeted me. She looked calm. I asked her how her mum was.

'Go see for yourself,' she replied. 'Out in the garden. I'll leave you two alone.'

The garden typified Margo's character. Tidy shrubs and rockeries decorated the upper tier. The lower tier was wild, with native gums adjoining a narrow stream, where a lizard was sunning itself on a rock, as birds quietly fluttered here and there. With the escarpment rising above, it seemed the perfect setting for being at one with nature.

Margo was seated in the shade on the upper tier. Facing the stream and the escarpment, she didn't see me as I walked from the patio. Despite her disease and dependency, Margo still looked reasonably well. As I approached her, she seemed completely absorbed in the beauty of her garden. There was something about her facial expression that I couldn't quite grasp: a stillness or an aura of gentleness. Noticing me, she smiled and in a moment of eye contact I suddenly realised what I saw in her. It was more than peace, more than happiness. It was profound contentment. She appeared 'at one' with the universe, and things were clearly different for her now compared with the troubled Margo of two weeks before. Returning the smile, I greeted her and sat down.

'Margo, you seem completely absorbed in the beauty of your garden.'

Still smiling through soft grey eyes, she replied, 'No, it is the beauty of my self that I am absorbed in.' She sighed happily and continued. 'In all these years that I have loved nature, I never realised it was my "self" that I was appreciating. I would go to the forest to feel peaceful, the sea to find beauty or the mountains to experience wonder. Every time I went somewhere like this I would become happy and uplifted. Only now have I understood why. I have realised that what I experienced in relation to nature was within myself. When I went to these places all the conflicts and problems of my life disappeared temporarily. When I looked in awe at a mountain the sight was free from sentiment, yet I experienced wonder.'

I must have been looking puzzled.

'Don't you see,' she said. 'The wonder was not in the mountain, it was in me! When we go to these places we become free from all the superficial things of life. This freedom makes our spirit happy and we experience love, peace and simplicity. If we could only learn to listen to our spirit then we could remain absorbed in its beauty.' She paused, slightly breathless from her lung disease.

'For all my life I have been dependent on nature to be happy. At least, up until now. It is as if I was searching on the outside for what made me feel good on the inside. You discover your soul when you find and appreciate your inner beauty. We must take peace from the forest and own it, because in truth it really belongs to us. Nature's gift is what it awakens in us.'

Margo seemed oblivious to a butterfly that had landed on the back of her hand. Lazily it opened and closed iridescent blue wings as she continued.

'I am going to die soon.' She smiled, then qualified her statement. 'Well, I am going across the threshold that some people call death. I would like to have lived a little longer to give this message to the world: *to appreciate that everything we really need is already within us*. At least I have discovered it for myself. Perhaps you could spread it around for me.'

'I'll write a book about it,' I joked. We laughed. 'You don't really need anything from me, do you?' I asked.

'No,' she replied. 'Just the book!'

As I walked away, I glanced back. The look of deep contentment had returned. She was beautiful and at peace with herself. The butterfly left her hand, hovered for a few moments, then flew away. Margo died two hours later.

～

I was deeply affected by Margo's contentment and its lesson: *appreciate your intrinsic beauty and you will become deeply contented.* We are coloured by the circumstances of our lives. Beautiful scenery in the absence of pressure draws peace, happiness and wellbeing to the surface. Difficult relationships, conflict and responsibilities make us feel trapped, tense or unhappy. It is as if, when a scene changes, our contentment can either surface or become merged within us. Imagine having the power to maintain it under any circumstances. Instead of being 'coloured', our contentment would have a positive influence on our world and relationships. As Margo said, we must take peace from the forest and own it, because in truth it really belongs to us.

When we have the awareness that real identity is soul, then this is expressed through spirituality in our attitudes, actions and relationships. Spirituality really means inner beauty made visible through the expression of virtues. If you relate *constantly* with peace, understanding, wisdom and mercy, then you will be influential on the basis of spirituality. Others will trust in your love and acceptance of them.

Appreciation involves looking for strengths beyond the mistakes and weaknesses we witness. All too often we look for, and speak of, the negative characteristics of others. We take 'on board' their negativity, spread it around with gossip and lose our peace of mind in doing so. We might feel justified, but what good has been done? Likewise, as our own weaknesses or mistakes hurt us, we tend to think more of these than of our qualities, strengths and virtues. The spiritual effort of appreciation is a decision to look only at virtues within the self and others. It is a decision to ignore the inner critic that says, *I'm no good* or *They're no good*.

Behind the facades of ego or arrogance, every human soul is beautiful. Body-conscious conditioning conceals spiritual love and innocence, enabling negativity to surface. Whatever the words or actions, beauty resides within, hidden away. However hard it is to believe at times, there are no exceptions. A key aspect to appreciating the beauty of your soul is to understand and accept this. As you discover this beauty within yourself, you will find it in others. If you refuse to see it in others, you will be unable to find it in yourself.

By seeking virtues in others, you learn more of the qualities they define and you are able to imbibe them for yourself. Say, for instance, that your boss is a successful businessman but his greed has affected his employees. He is also a very determined character who, by satisfying himself, has been using his determination in a negative and destructive way. Reacting to his greed by criticising his attitude and integrity, brings you into the arena of angry or jealous feelings. In 'choosing' this response you 'decide' to become 'peaceless', without influencing his behaviour. Furthermore, you are attacking a human soul who is lost and blind: lost behind the veils of body-consciousness and blinded by material desires. His greed has affected you and you have allowed your peace of mind to dissolve.

If, instead, you remain unaffected by his greed but absorb the quality of determination, then three things change in the relationship. First, you maintain your peace of mind; second, you add to your beauty by imbibing the virtue of determination; and third, you have *given* him regard by appreciating his quality.

Although the businessman has distorted the value of determination through greed, it is actually a surviving, still-visible virtue. It can still be seen in his personality and, in all likelihood, it is this *virtue* that has enabled him to succeed. We can think of it as one of the specialities of his soul.

With purer soul-conscious motives, determination is a virtue of divine purpose. Determination to see value in everything. Determination never to give sorrow to anyone. Determination to maintain a positive attitude. Determination to grow. If you take the quality and disengage it from the greed, then you learn about it, reawaken it in yourself and become more virtuous.

The pure state of soul-consciousness is complete with all divine virtues, whereas in body-consciousness, virtues become hidden or distorted. Fortunately, the distortion is not in the virtue itself but is in the motive with which it is used. The effort of appreciation is a spiritual endeavour of finding and expressing our virtues in a beneficial way. Like anything else, practice makes perfect. If I wanted to be good on the piano I would need to take lessons and practise regularly. At first it would require concentration and would feel awkward. In time, however, playing would become natural, with little need to think or concentrate. The same is true of virtues: they can be practised until they become a natural expression of ourselves.

As we reconnect with these original qualities, gentleness, respect and humility emerge with the courage and confidence to be ourselves. From this deep sense of self-respect we can give regard to others unconditionally, and become profoundly contented. As I experienced in Margo's company, such contentment is extremely attractive and influential. It is like a spiritual 'fragrance' that naturally serves others while you are simply being yourself.

In accepting only virtues from the outside world, we are learning to see differently. Both effort and attention are necessary to sustain this divine vision and to maintain the contentment it offers. In the next chapter we will look at the application of meditation to achieve this.

10

Meditation

Until I experienced spiritual love at the Kübler-Ross workshop, I was a confirmed atheist. Afterwards, by contrast, I believed that God had touched my life, revealing a quality of love that I should sustain and share with others. To hold and maintain this relationship with love, however, was to prove challenging.

To begin with, I changed two things in my life. The first was my career as a cancer specialist. Until the workshop, I had given little consideration to the suffering aspect of cancer. Afterwards, I had a genuine wish to relieve my patients' physical and emotional pain. With compassion awoken, serving others gave me pleasure and I was drawn to work with the dying. This brought me a sense of being more holistic and complete as a physician. The other change I made involved taking up meditation, so as to care for myself while caring for others. I found the balance of meditation and service to be a most effective way of nurturing love.

I taught myself to meditate by reading about it and practising daily. My aim was to feel connected in love to God, as this is what I believed I had experienced at the workshop. I used to sit on an escarpment close to my home overlooking a forest canopy and the ocean. On reflection, I am amused when I recall my intensity and desire for an experience of God. I would sit for an hour a day, eyes closed, trying to reach God. Generally I became very peaceful and contented, but I never had the rush of love that I experienced at the Kübler-Ross workshop.

One day it occurred to me that maybe God was trying to reach me, and all I had to do was allow Him or Her to do so. On that occasion I just opened my heart and, with a feeling of surrender, was immediately filled with love. This sense of 'allowing God' is subtly different because it was based 'on God's terms' rather than mine. I began to see that my own ego had been separating me from love and that this was a block I needed to address.

To guide my mind in a more spiritual direction, I started to read from uplifting texts for around twenty minutes during meditation. These put me in touch with my eternal identity, made me feel connected with God's love, and gave me a sense of serving humanity. During the day I would reflect on the morning reading, which kept the meditation experience alive through my working hours. I began thus to integrate spiritual values into daily living, which accords with the Eastern term for religion (dharma) that means 'way of life'.

About eight years after the workshop with Kübler-Ross, a doctor working under my supervision introduced me to some new concepts. She believed the soul could become impure and that it thinks, speaks and acts through the instrument or vehicle of the body. The original purity and peace of the soul is suppressed as its behaviour is conditioned by body-consciousness. She said that the soul becomes flawed and that meditation reverses this conditioning towards purity again. Meditation, she told me, is about channelling thoughts in the 'right' direction and about mastering our minds and senses. Thoughts are our creation and they determine how we feel. If they were not so influenced by the external world, and were less drawn towards various forms of sense-gratification, then we would feel peaceful and loving.

Although I resisted these ideas, they gradually made sense. I had believed the soul to be ever-pure and beyond worldly influence, just waiting for me to find it. Now I began to wonder *Who am 'I'?* and *Who is the soul?* I remember walking into a patient's room just after he had died. There was a distinct sense of the presence of that departed spirit. I could feel his personality in the room, yet the body was lifeless. The body had no attitudes, memories or identity without the soul; nor could it communicate. The soul had left with its individuality and personality intact. I now believed what my friend had told me and my question was answered: *I am a soul and I act through my body.*

The challenging thing about holding and maintaining a

relationship with love is that we constantly separate ourselves from it. Whenever we react to criticism, become angry or spread unkind gossip, we separate ourselves from love. Whenever we feel jealous or depressed, we separate ourselves from love. Whenever we are forceful or afraid, we separate ourselves from love. Meditation, as a way of life, changes the way we react and how we are influenced. On the basis of spiritual awareness and attitudes, it gives us the power to focus our minds in the positive direction of peace and happiness. If we stop the thoughts that create stress and negativity, then we are likely to have a beneficial influence on others without trying.

Meditation makes the mind receptive to love, not simply as an emotion but as a power to do good. So what can we do and what effort can we make to enable the soul to remain peaceful and connected with love? In my first encounter with unconditional love, love was my whole experience. For three weeks after the cathartic workshop, *I was love*. It was a state of being. Since 1992, I have practised Raja Yoga, a form of meditation that encourages one to transform negative characteristics, while adopting spiritual values. In this spiritual endeavour, the first step is to understand the mind, its qualities and its potential. The second is to heal oneself. And the third is to become love.

Developing virtues

In this meditation exercise I will first outline a way of entering meditation, then focus on the aspect of virtues. I have listed thirty-six virtues below, taken from my study of Raja Yoga meditation. These might prove useful as you concentrate on those you either feel familiar with or need to acquire.

Your divine virtues

Cheerfulness	Introspection	Maturity
Sweetness	Tolerance	Humility
Honesty	Mercy	Lightness
Fearlessness	Contentment	Patience
Wisdom	Self-confidence	Purity
Benevolence	Generosity	Truthfulness
Tirelessness	Obedience	Royalty (of self)
Accuracy	Surrender	Carefree
Courage	Discipline	Cleanliness
Stability	Gentleness	Determination
Detachment	Simplicity	Co-operation
Respect	Serenity	Flexibility

As we practise particular virtues we become more familiar with them and learn how to use them. Ultimately, the virtues empower our minds with the capacity to maintain equanimity while having constant good wishes for others.

To begin with, sit quietly and comfortably. If you already have a meditation technique, then enter meditation in the usual way. If not, then try the following ideas to relax the body and become peaceful. It is preferable to meditate with the eyes open, as what we learn is to be applied to everyday living.

Sit comfortably and with the body alert and symmetrical.

Let your mind first go over the body, relaxing each part, from the feet up. It can be helpful to tense and relax each part, and to experience the difference between tension and relaxation. As you proceed you will find yourself entering a progressively deeper state of relaxation.

Beginning with the feet, followed by the calves, first tense then relax the muscles, and feel the difference that relaxation brings. Next, the thighs: relax the muscles, letting the tension go; then the buttocks: tense the muscles and relax, letting the tension go. Allow the feeling of relaxation to spread through you.

Repeat this exercise on the stomach, the chest, the shoulders, the upper arms, the forearms and the hands. After tensing and relaxing the hands, spend a few moments just observing where they are resting, and feel deep relaxation spreading through you. Experience a feeling of letting all tension go. Now relax the neck, then the jaw: grit the teeth together tightly, then let the mouth hang slightly open. Next, the eyes. I always find this an amazingly relaxing sensation by this stage. Screw up the eyes tightly, hold the tension, then let it go. And finally the forehead: frown tensely and then let go.

Once the body is relaxed, sit for a few minutes absorbing yourself into the experience of relaxation. While in this state have the thought *I am a peaceful soul* and simply sit, observing how relaxed the body feels.

Next, go into experiencing a virtue or quality you would like to develop. Take for instance the virtue of tolerance. The stronger you are in this, the less likely you are to resort to anger. First, think about the quality, then go into its experience. There are several ways of doing this. If you are tolerant by nature then it is a quite accessible virtue and you can enter its experience directly. If it is less familiar, you can find it by visualising someone you know with a tolerant nature, and then enter the feeling of tolerance in that person's character. This draws your latent tolerance to the surface, and very soon you begin to experience the state of tolerance itself.

Once you are experiencing the quality, then consider its value. Again, there are several ways of doing this. You can imagine yourself in a situation where it is needed and visualise yourself using the quality effectively. Alternatively, remember a situation where you became angry. Bring that situation to mind, then imagine using tolerance and visualise a better outcome. In this you are not trying to change what happened but are converting a negative experience into one of learning.

In this way, through meditation, you practise and experience virtues, as well as learn how to use them. By becoming familiar with the qualities you need for different situations, they become much easier to access when challenged. In choosing to remain virtuous throughout the day, you will also find that you are much more in control of yourself.

For this exercise, first consider and then write down the virtues or qualities that are your strongest. You might like to refer to the list I have given or use your own words. The ones that feel familiar to you are your strongest virtues. Of the others, write down three or four you would particularly like to work on.

Apply the meditation exercise to one virtue at a time, beginning with the more familiar ones. It is useful to look up the dictionary definition, as this will give you a better feel for the nature and quality of each one. Spend fifteen or twenty minutes in the morning with the exercise. During the day, be aware of every time you use the virtue you are working on. In the evening spend another fifteen to twenty minutes of meditation or reflection to review the day. Go again into the experience of the virtue and feel what it was like to use it. Also review situations where it would have been useful (or where you should have used it), and visualise yourself applying it. It is good to keep a diary as a way of monitoring progress.

Once the method is familiar, apply it to a quality you need to develop. Remember, you already have this virtue and are really reawakening it.

Use the technique of visualising the quality in someone else, then experiencing it for yourself. Always include the phases of imagining its use, the awareness of when it is used through the day, and of evening review. Never be disappointed in yourself. See a 'failure' as an opportunity to learn. You will be amazed at how quickly this attention improves the quality of your daily life.

Always be positive, appreciate yourself, find and absorb the virtues of others and enjoy developing a new way of living.

11

Cultivating a positive attitude

The best diet for meditation is to feed positive thoughts and feelings to the mind. Making an effort to maintain a positive attitude is a feature of the journey of realisation. It is also a feature of lesser worldly ideals, such as acquiring wealth or staying healthy. In view of this application to the limited desires of body-consciousness, I feel that positive attitude has lost its meaning and purpose.

Veronica was a special person who developed metastatic melanoma in her late thirties. What began for her as a limited desire to beat cancer became a much greater adventure. When Veronica was told that she would die from the condition, she reacted at first with shock and disbelief, and then with determination. Strong willed, she was not going to accept this prognosis. She had too much to live for: a loving husband, two adolescent daughters, a good job and an extended network of friends and relatives rallying behind her.

She elected to fight, believing that she could beat cancer with a positive attitude and an altered lifestyle. Veronica and her husband, David, attended a retreat with a group of other cancer patients and their partners. They learnt about complementary approaches, including diet, meditation and 'attitudinal healing', while developing supportive bonds with others who believed in the potential for cure. Veronica left with the conviction that she could heal herself and was now armed with the knowledge, skills and techniques to do so.

Everyone agreed that Veronica had an extremely positive attitude. Her intelligence, balance and energy drew tremendous support from friends, relatives and connections. The congregation of her local church prayed for her healing, while David was a wonderful support. He took on new domestic duties, juiced fruits and vegetables for her 'anti-cancer' diet and created spaces for Veronica to meditate. Despite this there was a visible, relentless progression of secondary cancers, which were growing beneath the skin where she could see and feel them. For about a year they grew slowly and painlessly, without affecting her function or vitality. She felt good and maintained the strong conviction that any day, just around the corner, they would simply dissolve away. She never entertained the possibility of failure.

In the two months before I met her, the tumours had grown much more rapidly. She also lost her appetite and experienced a reduction in her energy and wellbeing. On account of increasing pain and loss of sleep, she had become uncharacteristically irritable with her family. Through all of this she never once considered that she would die of cancer.

As the pain got worse, simple pain-killers no longer helped and Veronica's local doctor persuaded her to try morphine. On our first consultation the following day, she was in complete despair. Though pain-free, she was devastated. As soon as I sat her down in the consulting room, she burst into tears. Not just ordinary crying, but the sobbing of hopelessness and failure.

Sitting beside her, David looked helpless and apologetic. To his credit he didn't say anything, understanding that a need was being met. Confronted by Veronica's conviction in healing he had bottled up the feeling that they were losing the battle.

As the sobbing subsided, I encouraged her to tell me where it had come from.

'The morphine,' she said.

'The morphine?'

'Yes, the morphine!' Her voice was angry now. 'It means that I have failed. Failed, failed, failed …!' On the fringe of losing control again, she made a huge effort and composed herself. 'Up until today, I have never, not even for a moment, thought I could die. Now I know the situation is hopeless … completely hopeless.' Desperation overshadowed her resignation.

I hesitated, unsure of the best response, then said, 'Veronica, I need to know all about this situation. Let's go back. Back to when you first noted a problem with your health. Do you feel you can go over this with me now?'

She nodded, actually grateful to leave her present predicament for a while. She went on to tell me the whole story, including their attendance at the retreat and her endeavour to beat cancer. She told me about her discipline with the anti-cancer diet, about her meditation and her faith, of how her church was praying for her, and of how good everyone had been to her. She was much calmer as we returned to the present.

I continued. 'Veronica, it seems to me that starting morphine was the final straw. The tumours kept growing, while your weight, energy and vitality were all deteriorating. Yet you maintained the conviction that you would be healed. With great determination you even withstood two months of severe pain but when you started the morphine it all hit home. Nothing had prepared you for the shock of realising that nothing had worked.'

'Yes. But it's more than that. I feel as if I have failed.'

'In what way?'

'I feel as if I have failed everyone, especially David and the girls. They've given so much support and commitment to my recovery and now I've let them down. All my friends, everybody who has been good to me. Everybody who has been praying for my recovery.'

A solitary tear rolled down David's cheek as Veronica continued. 'If only I'd tried harder. Tried harder for everyone. If only my faith were stronger. I'm just not good enough. Now

I've made everyone's life miserable. I feel so … so helpless. And so worthless. It's like everything I've been doing for the last year was for nothing.' She paused, apparently finished.

I asked quietly, 'Has anything positive come out of your cancer experience?'

Wiping her eyes, she looked surprised and thought for a moment. 'Well, yes,' she began, 'my daughter is much closer to me now. We used to fight but she's been fantastic. It's as if she's grown up. She's so sensitive and considerate now. And David …' — she glanced in his direction, their eyes meeting in love and appreciation — 'Our relationship wasn't really the best before I was diagnosed. But he's been wonderful, and we've grown really close again. It's been lovely.'

'So it's drawn the whole family together,' I said.

She considered this for a moment, then said, 'And I've changed. I've become much easier-going. The things I used to worry about just pass me by now. I'm not so bothered by what people think. It's just great to be alive each day. I really appreciate life now. A sunrise, a bird singing, a moment of intimacy. My values have changed and I've grown a lot.'

She sparkled as another idea occurred to her. 'David's changed too. He's contented with simpler things, not so materially driven and much more giving as a person. We've both grown through the last year. More so, perhaps, than we could have done in a whole lifetime without the cancer.'

Enjoying herself now, Veronica continued. 'And another thing, I've really felt close to God in the last twelve months. I've always had faith as a Catholic, but now I really feel like

I have a *relationship* with God. It's as if Jesus has walked into my life, and is showing me new and wonderful things.'

As she stopped speaking on this note, Veronica seemed peaceful. Reassured. There was not a trace of the sorrow she had been experiencing only a few moments ago. As she looked at me, I felt it was my turn to speak.

'Veronica, I feel that everything you've done in the last year has been a success. The disease has progressed, and yes, it is catching up with you. But there has been so much growth and transition for you all.' I spent the next few minutes affirming the value of all her efforts. 'You have strengthened your will through discipline, diet and lifestyle changes. You have become more peaceful and contented through your meditation. Your attitude has both supported and guided your family. And you have realised the true declaration of faith to be a relationship with God.'

After a pause I continued. 'But you were so focused on making the cancer go away that you didn't notice these things. By making the cancer a yardstick of success or failure, you didn't fully appreciate the meaning of healing.

'I believe that a disease may come to make us grow in some way. Cancer can move you along spiritually, with or without your awareness. You have experienced healing in spite of the relentless progression of your cancer. So continue what you have been doing. Relax the diet, perhaps, to relieve pressure. But do everything now with more balanced objectives between spiritual and physical healing. By all means remain hopeful of remission, but let this be a bonus.

'Your healing can continue even if the disease progresses. If you have to die young it is worth realising that few elderly people achieve what you have. The benefits of your growth and spiritual knowledge will influence your family. You will continue to model and shape their lives, even when you are no longer here for them.'

Sitting together we all felt somehow connected and up-lifted. Veronica was euphoric. She had come to see me in a state of despair and devastation. She had felt a complete failure. During the consultation, we discovered that her yard-stick of success or failure had been whether or not she died of cancer. A reorientation towards spiritual objectives had given her another way of looking at healing, and her entire philosophy had been validated.

Veronica subsequently let go of her fear of death and her spirituality enriched everyone before she 'left'. She personi-fies the value of including spiritual objectives whenever we aim to be positive.

~

Thoughts are the seeds of what we experience. If we could train the mind to think only positive thoughts then we would experience life accordingly. When Veronica was diagnosed she set out with the thought *I can beat cancer*. For twelve months she was radiantly positive despite having a concealed fear of dying. Morphine unveiled this fear when the thought of the cancer winning brought overwhelming despair. When Veronica replaced her mortal attitude of failure with the thought *I am a soul, fulfilling the spiritual purpose of my life*, she experienced deep joy, satisfaction and acceptance. Nothing had changed except that her attitude now reflected spiritual immortality, and she was free from the limited aim of staying healthy.

This reflects the main effort needed to sustain a positive attitude, which is to remember and affirm *I am a soul, fulfilling the spiritual purpose of my life*. This also involves an endeavour to express ourselves according to such awareness at all times, under all circumstances.

Becoming positive

Positive thoughts, words and actions benefit others, make us feel good and create a good atmosphere. Negative thoughts, words and actions have the opposite effect. They hurt others and spoil the atmosphere.

Selecting what we do represents a function of the intellect, which is a filter between thinking (the mind) and acting (the body). The intellect 'governs' the mind through its capacity to discern, to judge and to decide. A positive attitude emerges when we use the intellect to express spiritual purpose in thoughts, words, actions and relationships.

First discern truth from falsehood, then judge what conforms to spiritually right action, before deciding how to act. Training oneself to discern, judge and act in this way expresses spirituality. Truly positive people are revealed when their decisions consistently result in three principal outcomes:

- they remain contented and bring peace, happiness and contentment to others;
- they co-operate and thereby encourage others to be co-operative;
- they promote spiritual awareness on the basis of their personality and actions.

When we apply ourselves to these aims we are able to evaluate our progress. By observing the results of our words and actions, we can review the quality of our decision-making and judgement: 'Did I bring about peace, co-operation or spiritual awareness?' If we make mistakes, we learn from them and strengthen our minds. In this way we see that our mistakes have a purpose rather than believing that we are failing.

Even with a spiritual attitude, it may be difficult to conform in our actions. There is a reason for this. Actions are also influenced by our nature and personality, which include the following three obstacles to spiritual progression:

- acquired habits, dependencies and personality traits;
- self-centredness; and
- prejudice.

Latent within us is an original, pure personality, which has been gradually conditioned through life experiences. What evolves are habitual patterns, dependencies, ego and prejudice, which begin to override the intellect on how we think and behave. Our ability to discern, judge, decide and act spiritually weakens, and conditioning ultimately influences the expression of the soul. The effort to become positive is one of renewing the dominance of intellect over conditioning, and one of reawakening soul-consciousness.

Beginning with the thought *I am a soul, fulfilling the spiritual purpose of my life*, we can focus and strengthen the intellect. At the same time we exercise control over our prejudices, and over the habit of seeing weaknesses in others. To achieve this we must first become observers of our own attitudes and actions, then endeavour to bring peace, co-operation and truth into the world. In effect, we become peaceful and develop a nature of love and simplicity, which is not influenced by the negativity of others.

Affirming your true identity

In this exercise, enter meditation in the same way as outlined in Chapter 10. Once you are in meditation, affirm to yourself, *I am a peaceful soul (spirit, light energy, eternal being), fulfilling the spiritual purpose of my life*. Make these positive thoughts of identity and purpose firm. They are quiet internal affirmations of love for your true self. Repeat them in your mind, then pause into lengthy silences and let yourself experience the positive feelings and emotions they bring.

Spend ten to fifteen minutes with this exercise at the beginning of the day, then one to two minutes every two hours throughout the day, and finally ten minutes before bed at night.

Be disciplined initially and you will find it becomes a pleasure. Pleasure makes it habit-forming, so that it is transformed from a disciplined activity to a desirable activity.

Observing your thoughts, feelings and actions

This exercise should be conducted throughout the day. It involves self-control, internal review and preparation for confronting circumstances. The aim is to remain positive in actions, and to be aware of negative thoughts or emotions.

Holding onto the affirmations of the previous exercise, determine to have positive thoughts for yourself and others. Observe the effects of your words and actions throughout the day. Evaluate or discern whether they bring about one of our three aims:

- to make others more peaceful, happy or contented;
- to bring about co-operation; or
- to create self-awareness.

Initially, this discernment may follow an event when you realise that you acted without thinking. According to your nature or habits you may have reacted to something under the influence of arrogance, anger or selfish desire. Try to be aware of the feelings you have after performing right or wrong actions, but be an observer. Remember, you are trying to gradually correct rather than punish yourself. As the first step you are coming to know your own mind better.

Recognise, in particular, when you have used discernment, judgement and decision-making effectively. Progressively you will find greater consistency in being positive, as the intellect strengthens its control over your actions. Be aware in advance of what you might need in a confronting situation and prepare yourself for it. In particular 'arm' yourself with virtues, such as tolerance, patience and respect for the self and others. This will prevent you from coming under the influence of strong personal desires for a particular outcome, and keep you centred on being spiritual.

~

As you knowingly use the powers of the intellect, and connect with your virtues, you will find that others become co-operative. Not immediately perhaps, but in time. Eventually, through this training of the mind, you will automatically respond to situations correctly. You will not have to go through preparation. The training actually makes you *ever-ready* such that, when conflict comes without warning, you are completely stable, unaffected and accurate.

As part of this retraining of the mind, I recommend daily review of how positive you have been. It is useful to keep a written chart or diary to this end, which will give you a record of progress over time. Always consider 'failures' to have been lessons whose purpose is to make you stronger. Review what happened. Were you weak in discernment, judgement or decision-making? Did you come under the influence of fear, old habits or a personality trait? Did you react under the influence of greed, anger or ego? Did you feel compelled to carry out an action even though you had discerned it to be hurtful? Consider the influence behind the compulsion, for this is a habit you can change through your awareness of it.

Maintain a positive and nurturing approach to yourself. Concentrate on your effectiveness and increase your awareness when there are 'failures'. If you turn an obstacle into a learning experience in this way, then you have successfully transformed it to love.

Freeing yourself from negativity

Waste and negativity begin with a thought that is either useless or vindictive. The experience created actually separates us from love. Wasteful thought patterns such as thinking about situations and people you can't change, worrying about the future or wishing that you could change the past are harmless but serve no purpose. Why waste time and energy thinking or talking about the actions or attitudes of others? Negativity relates to vindictive or hurtful thoughts, words or actions that cause suffering in the self or others.

In this chapter we are looking at the important effort of *being* positive. We are also considering how life experience conditions our nature and attitudes. In effect, we are looking at the whole energy that now defines our consciousness. It is the capacity to think, to decide, to express and to record memories or experiences.

This defines the self as a living, conscious energy that acts through the body. I have, on occasion, had a distinct sense of 'presence' while examining a body immediately after death. I have felt that the one who recently left was still close by. This has led me to believing that everything that defines personality is in the soul. Certainly it is not in the bodies I examine. Whatever was living has gone and is still living.

In 1992, I encountered Raja Yoga meditation and its philosophy of the soul. It felt like I had stumbled on something that was accurate and simple. Essentially it goes like this: 'I am a soul and not a body, my original nature was peace and everything experienced or expressed is a faculty of the soul.' According to Raja Yoga, a soul or spirit contains three 'organs' that express consciousness — namely, the conscious mind, the intellect and the *sanskaras* (subconscious mind, nature or personality).

Sanskara is an Eastern term, which relates to an impression or imprint left on the soul by a past action or experience. The original nature of a soul is pure and innocent, before it develops the sanskaras of negative encounters. Under the influence of these, the soul itself develops a capacity for fear and impure thoughts, tendencies or feelings. The soul itself becomes body-conscious as wasteful and negative patterns emerge.

These sanskaras condition and change our personalities. As they accumulate they affect the soul like rust on a shiny needle, hiding its original purity and sparkle. The effort-making required to free yourself from waste and negativity is about removing this 'rust' and rediscovering your original purity.

Now imagine the mind as a garden where wasteful thoughts and negativity are weeds; left untended these overgrow and choke all that is beautiful. Wise gardeners cultivate the beauty of a garden, with flowers and plants that prevent weeds from growing. They then keep it under constant surveillance, removing the occasional weed before it becomes established. More careless gardeners allow the garden to become overgrown, then spend two thankless days of labour pulling out the weeds. After experiencing satisfaction for a few days, they let it get out of hand again, and the cycle repeats.

The spiritual aspirant could be viewed in this way. As a gardener of the mind, they would be wise to cultivate beauty and balance. Weeds are controlled under a 'ground-cover' of stability, tolerance and patience, while the seeds of virtue are planted to make the 'garden' bloom. Through regular careful surveillance, wasteful or negative thoughts are pruned before they come into expression.

We have already considered the spiritual efforts of positive attitudes and appreciation. From the garden of the mind we can see that these efforts contribute to eliminating the weeds of negativity. In this section, we will now focus on transforming wasteful thoughts and negativity through being detached and being responsible.

Being detached

Spiritual detachment does not mean distancing ourselves or becoming coldly dissociated from others. On the contrary, it reflects a sense of self that is neither influenced by the negativity of others, nor affected by circumstances that would otherwise have caused distress, fear or reactivity. By looking through the 'eyes' of self-knowledge, we understand that people act under the influence of body-consciousness and it is their body-consciousness that we try to detach from.

Consider my work with the terminally ill, where I come into intimate relationship with people facing death, loss and separation from all that they love. In my role as a physician I can offer much-needed help with pain control, but I also try to enter each such relationship with spiritual awareness. When I succeed in this I find that I am lighter, more relaxed and attentive, and more responsive to the person's suffering.

Through self-awareness I automatically sense the eternal nature of others and witness suffering as a temporary phase of spiritual adjustment. This brings a feeling of closeness and empathy, without being distressed or reactive. I find that people will then 'open up', so that I can understand their physical, emotional or spiritual needs more deeply. So spiritual awareness brings detachment from suffering yet leads to a warmer, closer and more loving relationship.

Whatever the beliefs of someone frightened by death, they will be comforted by the company of faith — that is, by the presence of quiet spiritual awareness. Such presence is an expression in itself that all is well in destiny; you need not even say a word. To be detached in this way allows you to see others as they are, and enables you to discern their needs appropriately.

When it is a projection of spiritual awareness, detachment enables us to become non-judgemental observers. By understanding that vindictive attitudes come from body-consciousness, we develop a merciful outlook in which we accept people as they are. Except through example there is no need to interfere with the attitudes or destiny of others, and no need to waste time contemplating negative thoughts about them.

With such acceptance, trust and understanding, we can develop a profound state of self-respect. This enables us to face our weaknesses without feeling hurt or angry when someone faults our words or actions. Some years ago, when working as a palliative care registrar, I was asked to see the wife of a retired medical colleague. She had advanced bowel cancer, with secondary spread to the liver. As she was too unwell to come to the hospital, I arranged to visit them at home. My colleague met me at the door and asked to speak to me for a few minutes first. He told me that he had kept the knowledge of cancer from her, and asked me not to discuss it with her.

The consultation went well. She didn't seem to want to know what was wrong with her and I was effective in relieving her pain. Several weeks later I was called again. There had been a considerable deterioration, and she was troubled by constant nausea. When I arrived at the home, I could see that things were pretty desperate. She was severely wasted, bedbound and deeply jaundiced (yellow) from liver failure.

On this occasion she asked, 'Do you think I will get better?' Remembering she had been kept in the dark, I replied with a question. 'Well, how do things appear to you? How have you been recently?'

'Terrible,' she said. 'I'm sick all the time. I'm getting weaker. And I can hardly do anything for myself …' She paused. 'So, will I get better?'

Perhaps she was looking for reassurance. However, I felt she was trying to understand what was happening to her and wanted an honest answer.

'I'm sorry,' I said, 'but I don't think you will get better. There's a bit of a problem with your liver, and I think it's getting worse.'

'How do you know that?'

I noticed the anxiety of her voice and body language. As gently as possible I answered, 'There's a tinge of yellow visible in your eyes and skin. It's a sign.' I was being a master of understatement: she was as yellow as a lemon.

Tears rolled down her cheeks. 'I'm going to die, aren't I?'

'I'm sorry, but I think you may,' I replied. 'I think it's to do with the old cancer problem. It seems to have flared up a bit, in the liver.'

'What can you do for me?' she asked.

'First of all, I can get rid of this nausea trouble you've been having …' I went on to assure her that we would be able to deal with any new problems, that she would not suffer from excessive pain and that we would help her towards a peaceful passage from this life to the next.

A couple of days later, I telephoned to check whether my prescription had settled the vomiting. It had, but my medical colleague's voice was disapproving. I felt uncomfortable but asked if he would like me to review her progress in a week or so.

He said, 'No thank you, Dr Cole, you are no longer welcome here, so goodbye and please don't call again.'

I was stunned. I felt like a train had hit me in the pit of the stomach. Had I been insensitive or, worse still, incompetent? As I went through the rest of the day my mind was unable to function effectively; I couldn't stop going over and over the situation. Intellectually I felt I had done my job, but my emotions were in turmoil.

Hurt and full of self-doubt, I went straight to the ward, needing to successfully relieve someone's suffering and to have that recognised. Despite being seen as someone with relatively high self-esteem, I needed to be validated, to hear a patient tell me that I was wonderful, and that I had made everything much clearer.

If I had possessed greater self-respect, the phone call would not have influenced me. After all, my patient had asked for honesty and I had responded in a necessary way. She needed to know, otherwise how could she understand why life was so bad for her? Self-respect, or the deep acceptance of self, is a form of humility that expresses automatic regard for everyone. Had I possessed this I would have been firm in my feeling that I had done the best I could. Even if I had made a mistake, I would have seen this as an opportunity to learn rather than experience despair. When there is self-respect and humility, there is no room for waste or negativity.

Spiritual detachment means to possess a strong sense of self, which is not influenced by the negativity of others. It is a way of loving others as eternal beings and of understanding that they too have been deceived by body-consciousness.

To consider that everything resides within a divine plan is another aspect of spiritual detachment. Think for a moment of the world as a huge stage where each soul is an actor with a unique and accurate part to play. An actor plays his or her own part without concern for the roles of others. Concentrating on his own role, he or she simply observes and interacts with the roles of others, never trying to take on their parts. You can become an observer of the drama of life in this way. I believe we live in a complex age but have the conviction that it is a benevolent drama, even when the scenes contain suffering or pain. Imagine you are sitting in a cinema being entertained by each scene. There is a reason for everything. Through soul-consciousness you see it all differently and understand that immortality leaves no room for worry, fear or concern. This brings a sense of higher purpose and prevents negative thoughts and feelings from emerging.

Being responsible

The second aspect of freeing yourself from negativity is that of taking responsibility. I recently spoke with a meditation teacher who was lamenting an error with two students. They had been attending a group programme run by my friend. They were really interested in the philosophy expressed, and wanted to experience peace and positivity in their lives. They committed themselves to a five-week course in meditation. As a couple, they seemed enthusiastic, but turned up late on the first night. They did so again on the second, disrupting the group with a lame excuse. After the session my friend confronted them. She told them that they would only find peace, and a positive attitude, if they took more responsibility for themselves. They never returned.

My friend felt that she had been too hard on them and had

offended them. There may have been some truth in this, but it also demonstrates a limitation common to the world today. Many people who are drawn towards peace and spirituality are unwilling to *be* responsible for themselves. Once they find that it can't be done for them, and that they have to engage disciplines to change themselves, they lose interest. People want peace, but they want a quick fix in a quick-fix society. They also want to blame others for their 'peace-lessness', saying things like:

'I got angry because so and so said ...'

'It's not my fault.'

'They made me do it.'

Until we begin to be responsible for our actions, our feelings and responses, we will continue to be the victims of our circumstances. When we become responsible, and cease to blame, we are engaging the efforts of self-transformation. Instead of blaming someone else after a bout of anger it is better that we take responsibility, resolve to change and thereby increase our power of tolerance. Such responsibility brings greater self-control and is an act of love, which nurtures growth.

12

Letting go

In Chapter 5, Margaret found acceptance before dying of cancer. By letting go completely, accepting her destiny and yielding to circumstance she became the embodiment of love and surrender. Through the use of meditation we can apply this lesson and discover how to surrender. In Raja Yoga this is termed 'dying alive', which really means that our old nature dies through self-realisation. The spiritual effort of letting go is the key to this process.

At forty-seven, Maria was relatively young to be dying of cervical cancer. She was a slightly built Chinese Buddhist, who had a husband and two children, aged ten and fourteen. She had presented three years earlier with vaginal bleeding from a small cancer of the cervix. Following a hysterectomy she remained well, put the cancer experience behind her and

returned to a normal lifestyle. Two months before being trans-
ferred to my care she had a recurrence of cancer in the pelvis.
It was extensive, involving the bladder, rectum and pelvic
side-wall. Though incurable, a surgeon offered aggressive
treatment, in which he operated and removed all that he
could, including the rectum and bladder. Maria was left with
two bags on the front of her abdomen, one for urine and the
other for faeces. She was given six weeks of post-operative
radiotherapy.

She never really recovered from this. She progressively
lost weight, energy and wellbeing, and never returned to
work. When she arrived in the hospice she was withdrawn,
very depressed, in severe pain and surrounded by an offen-
sive odour. We initially relieved her pain and started her on
antibiotics to reduce the odour.

I subsequently visited her twice a week. She was in a miserable, despairing, hopeless state of mind. Each time I asked
how she was feeling, she replied, 'I can't bear this. I don't
want to live any more. Please end it for me now.'

From time to time people make such requests. Generally,
I've found that it's more a way of expressing hopelessness
than a genuine request for euthanasia. In Maria's case it was
both genuine and firm; she definitely wanted me to end her
life and looked at me with expectation. On each visit I asked
her why it was so unbearable that she wanted to die.

She replied, 'I'm so disgusting.' She couldn't bear to look at
the bags on her abdomen. 'I'm useless, worthless and there's
no point to my life. I have no energy, I can't do anything, I'm

not a woman and I hate myself. No one can help me.' When I asked her how this made her feel, she said, 'So unhappy, so unhappy,' then started to cry. She told me that she couldn't bear seeing her husband and children because they reminded her of how happy she had once been, and she felt jealous that they were well.

Talking to her family, I discovered that her husband was feeling really helpless and that her children were grieving and feeling rejected. On each visit I first listened to her feelings and perspectives before telling her that I couldn't end her life. She accepted this, saying that she had appreciated the opportunity to talk it over.

For six weeks we had exactly the same discussion, twice a week. It seemed that she needed to keep expressing it. During this period we arranged for her to have weekend leave and go home with her family. To our disappointment it was a disaster. We had hoped it would make her feel better and help to rebuild her relationships. On the contrary, she returned more depressed and had distanced herself further from her children. They were in a state of emotional turmoil. On the plus side, Maria and I had developed a good relationship and her depression had been lightening. It was at this time that I explored her spiritual beliefs. She seemed happier after talking about her religion and agreed to a pastoral visit from a Buddhist monk.

Over the next two weeks she became happy and stopped requesting euthanasia. She said that she felt contented and ready to die when it was her time. Much to their relief she now welcomed visits from her husband and children. Instead of the previous tension and withdrawal, we would find them with their arms around each other, beaming at one another.

On one of my visits I asked her how the monk had made such a difference.

'He told me that disease is a result of past karma (actions),' she said, 'and that I had to accept it. He said it was a cleansing process, which was preparing me for spiritual ascendancy in my next birth. I now understand that I am settling some old karmic accounts, which is part of becoming a free spirit.'

I was relieved by this development. Through finding meaning, her anger and sorrow had dispersed. She now had a purpose, and spiritual 'knowledge' had given her self-respect.

She continued. 'He said that the greater my equanimity, the less my spirit would struggle before taking rebirth. He told me to stop making my family suffer. He made me see that I would stop feeling that I was disgusting to them by not feeling disgusted with myself.'

He went on to talk to her of the Buddhist philosophy of impermanence. Everything changes; nothing stays the same. Suffering results from trying to hold on to what must change. Individual life, he said, is a series of changing relationships through different births. We might meet again at different times but never in the same way. Everything we have is impermanent and temporary, yet we hold on to everything for security or happiness and live in fear of loss. We become trapped in a web of attachments where loss is inevitable because nothing can remain the same.

'He told me to let go,' Maria said. 'To let go of all my attachments, which he said was the true road to freedom and happiness. So I have been doing this, letting go of my attachment to health, to the things I used to enjoy doing, to my family and to the future that I expected to have. Once he put it all in perspective for me, it became easy. I've never felt freer or happier than I do now.'

Maria lived for another three weeks before stepping peacefully into the afterlife. With her Buddhist counsellor present, she left her body without anxiety, concern or agitation.

Attachments are developed because we need security, comfort and happiness. But wherever there is attachment there is also dependence. This makes it very challenging to let go, so it is important to know what we are letting go of. In *The Tibetan Book of Living and Dying*, Sogyal Rinpoche gives a beautiful example of its meaning.[3] Consider, for a moment, that your hand is closed tightly around a coin. If you stretch out your arm and let go of the coin, palm down, it falls to the ground and you lose it. If you do the same thing with your palm facing up, you let it go yet it remains with you.

In the same way, letting go does not mean having to lose something. It is not our actual health, wealth or relationships that we let go of, it is being dependent on them. Dependency is an aspect of ego and body-consciousness, while letting go is an aspect of becoming soul-conscious. Being able to free ourselves from dependency begins when we recognise our spirit, and have faith in our immortality. Like clouds that obscure sunlight, attachment and dependency bring temporary happiness but keep us in the shadow of spiritual ignorance. When we let go we emerge from the shadows and see the light.

Letting go also means ceasing to be affected by what happened in the past, or concerned about what might happen in the future. This can be very challenging for those who have been hurt badly, or for those who are faced with uncertainty. To be free from the past we need to forgive, and to be free from the future we need to trust.

I couldn't recount the number of times I have heard a patient or family member say, 'I will never forgive ... and I will never forget.' Yet the memory they choose to hold on to is causing them sorrow and anger. They are still suffering from the past and seem unable to find reconciliation or peace. It's a great challenge to forgive people who have traumatised us. In the first instance we may feel that they don't deserve to be forgiven. Yet, unless we forgive, we can't forget. And, unless we forget, we can't free ourselves from their influence. In a sense they still have us trapped from the distance.

Perhaps we could start with the question, 'Do I deserve to be free from that person or situation?' The answer, of course, is, 'Yes, because I was innocent.' Forgiveness is really an attitude that frees the self and enables us to forget. It doesn't need to be spoken or written unless you find this helps. Although it may not affect or change those who hurt you, it finishes their ongoing power over your wellbeing. In the strangest of ways, if you learn this lesson, then the person who hurt you has made you stronger.

To be free from guilt we sometimes need to forgive ourselves. Although we can't change what we did we can resolve to learn from the mistake. Forgive yourself and let go, but don't forget. The memory will caution and prevent you from acting wrongly again. By turning mistakes into learning, forgiveness develops within us an attitude that is loving and non-judgemental. This, in turn, enables our love to flow effortlessly to others.

To live in the moment we must trust in the future and let go of expectations, worry or concern about how things might turn out. Let go of needing things to work out for you. By all means make plans, then live in the present and let the future come to you. By trusting in whatever happens we are unconditional, unattached and free from dependency. Try to see that everything is in divine order and that when things go wrong they were meant to. Sometimes this requires complete faith in the spiritual dimension, in the temporary nature of suffering and in some form of creative higher power. Trust brings us closer to the liberated, free and happy state of mind that characterises acceptance.

The spiritual effort of letting go is a progressive surrender of ego, which leads to one final, subtle thread of attachment. This final trace of arrogance or body-consciousness is the consciousness that says 'I' or 'mine', reflecting possessiveness or the desire for regard and recognition.

'What did you say about *my* daughter?'

'*I* should have been consulted.'

'That's *mine*, leave it alone.'

'*I* did it.'

The subtlety of this consciousness is deceptive. Even with substantial surrender, the desire for your name to be known or for someone to speak highly of you can persist. It is a delicate veil that we may not recognise, yet it deceives us and leads us away from all that is divine.

A method to free yourself from this final aspect of attachment is to consider yourself a trustee of possessions and relationships, while living as a 'guest' in this world.

Being a trustee and a guest

In this exercise we will endeavour to cultivate the habit of being a trustee and a guest in this world.

Nothing belongs to a trustee and a guest always has good and respectful manners. When something is loaned, rather than owned, it is taken better care of and used properly. We will experiment with the idea that everything 'I' have, in terms of my body, wealth, possessions and relationships, really belongs to the divine. Instead of owning these things, I have been entrusted with them to use on behalf of the divine. We will also experiment with the idea that, wherever 'I' am, I am a guest in the 'household' of the divine, behaving with divinity.

What you relate to as 'the divine' is up to you. For me it is God, who I see as a radiant point of light, love, knowledge and purity, who resides beyond our universe yet relates like a mother, father, friend and teacher. For you the form and location of the divine may differ from my reference. If you don't believe in an external manifestation, then look to the divine within the self. At least you know that you exist, so consider the divine to be your 'higher self'. For the purpose of this exercise I will refer to 'the divine', and leave the interpretation to you.

See everything you have as belonging to the divine; as a trustee become an instrument, using whatever you have to spread the influence of spirituality through pure feelings and good wishes; as a guest become a welcome and influential observer of the scenes of drama. As for previous exercises, begin with morning meditation, pay attention throughout the day and review your process at night.

Sitting in a comfortable position, enter meditation as previously described. Relax, let your attention go to the body and develop this awareness of letting go: 'This body is a vehicle on loan from the divine. I am a trustee of this body and a guest in this world.'

Sit in this state of awareness until it feels firm. If you prefer, use some other words, symbols or images of your own. Then extend the idea to all your possessions:

Nothing belongs to me. Everything I have belongs to the divine, and has been given for the purpose of service. Whatever I have is to bring peace or happiness. I am a guest even of my own household.

Next extend it to your roles. Let all your roles unfold in front of you. Sometimes you are a parent, sometimes a child, sometimes a spouse, sometimes a worker in your job or profession, sometimes a home-maker. Let go of all these roles with the thought:

These roles belong to the body and the responsibilities belong to the divine. As a trustee, living as a guest among spiritual brothers and sisters, I play my part. The divine uses everything I do, to reach everyone I know.

Let the world appear in your mind's eye like a huge stage on which an enormous drama is being enacted. While a trustee of your body, amid the influences of your life, you are a guest here also. The divine is the writer and director of the drama, and you are playing your part. You are a guest of the divine, and a guest in the drama. Detached and peaceful, you let the scenes of the world-play entertain you. There is nothing you have to do except surrender within an accurate and divine drama.

Allow yourself to experience that all responsibilities belong to the divine, and that your only responsibility is to stay within divine influence. Consider all others to be children of the divine who, like you, are guests in the drama, playing their unique and individual roles. No one belongs to you. In life you may be playing the role of a mother or a father, but your child is also a soul, so is really your 'brother' or 'sister'. And, like you, that soul is a child and a guest here. Let go of any feelings of possessiveness. No one belongs to you, though you may have been entrusted with their care. So be loving as an instrument of the divine.

Throughout the day take this attitude with you. *Nothing is mine. I am playing a part in a divine plan. Nobody belongs to me. Dependency is an illusion, created when I forgot who I belonged to.*

Be merciful with these thoughts. Stay detached and loving in the drama of life. Everything is divine. Nothing is wrong. The divine is responsible, and will make everything good with the co-operation of your surrender.

Being loving and detached

This meditation can be used concurrently with the other exercises we have covered. Together they offer a variety of ways to focus on different yet related aspects of spiritual growth. What I hope to demonstrate is that growth is a disciplined, constant self-training process. With the variety on offer through these exercises, I hope you will find refreshing ways to experiment with self-realisation.

As with the previous meditation exercises there are three components:

* meditation;
* discernment through the day;
* review.

In the first part we will focus on self-respect and accepting others. Enter meditation as outlined previously. Once you have relaxed for ten minutes or so, let someone enter your mind. Someone you have difficulty with. Perhaps not the most difficult person in your life as it might be a bit hard to start there! Maybe someone you like to avoid, or someone you react to when you see them coming. The sort of person you hope didn't see you when you pretended not to notice them. Or someone who takes up your time and seems oblivious to your needs.

You have an established pattern of relating to this individual, and this is common to all of us. We categorise souls, putting them into boxes labelled friend, foe, associate, annoying, arrogant, stupid, good, bad and so on. We react immediately to them in accordance with these labels. Once categorised, we tend to keep them in their box, with the lid firmly closed on those we dislike. To accept people as they are, we need first to remove the labels and let them out of the boxes. Second, we must acquire the habit of not labelling people altogether.

Now visualise or imagine your person to be in a box, with the lid on. Take a look at the box in your mind. Can you see the label? Then think to yourself, *If I let you go, you can be yourself, and I can also be free in our relationship.*

Now imagine yourself removing the label. Do so with the forgiving thought, *You are only like this because there have been losses in your life. I understand now that you have forgotten who you are.*

Allow this awareness to create the feeling that you should free this person from your box. Don't open the lid unless this feeling and the awareness are well developed. Once the feeling is well cultivated, open the box and imagine that the person is happy and liberated from the prison of your mind. As they appear happy, accept them completely with this thought:

I know you now as a soul. You are a traveller like me. Farewell, my friend.

Let them go from your mind, then review how it felt to do so. It is a good feeling. Within it you experience greater self-respect, having overcome a weakness in yourself that had made you body-conscious towards the nature of another.

~

This exercise makes you more soul-conscious, as you forgive someone's behaviour by understanding that it has been conditioned by sorrow. Work on one person at a time and you will witness remarkable results. Relationships will change. You will stop reacting in the predetermined way, having freed yourself from being so affected. These people will also respond to you in a more satisfactory way. Having done this exercise earnestly with a few people, you will find that something remarkable happens. Your habit of labelling people ends and you become tolerant of the way people are.

In a way, these labels have 'protected' you from feeling vulnerable, upset or angry. As you let them go, you are really letting go of your own fear and *learning how to love*. You learn to accept people as they are and become non-judgemental. With greater wisdom and understanding, it automatically follows that your self-respect deepens. This in turn strengthens you in the face of criticism, and enables you to become stable in fluctuating circumstances.

In association with this meditation exercise, tackle the day as an observer of the drama. See everything that happens as 'meant to be' or as a lesson. Remember that your detachment serves others by promoting peace and contentment. As you learn to detach and observe, you will become more spiritually discerning, wise and accurate. You will know when to speak and when to keep quiet. You will come to understand people better. And with this knowledge, you will learn how to support people so that they may grow.

Become an observer when you are criticised or praised. Respond appropriately but allow a sense of detachment to leave you less affected. It is easier in the beginning to control your reaction to praise. As you achieve this, self-respect becomes automatic (not needing regard from others) and you find yourself less affected by criticism.

As an observer you are keeping yourself under review and developing a stage of being introverted. This is a means of moving towards wisdom and self-control. Review the day internally and learn the lessons of 'failures' by seeing them as the hidden facilitators of growth. Remember that when you are making effort there must be 'failure' along the way. Otherwise no effort would be required!

13

Divine union

Paula is a 51-year-old divorcee who will have left her body by the time you read this. Diagnosed with metastatic bowel cancer twelve months before I saw her, she resolved not to accept her doctor's prognosis of a few months to live. Determined to beat the disease, she sought advice about complementary medicine from a former cancer patient. As a result, she changed her lifestyle, took various herbs and adopted a meditation programme.

Like Veronica in Chapter 11, she wouldn't entertain the prospect of failure. She had several operations for recurrent disease, followed by a period of increasing pain and weakness. Her quality of life had recently deteriorated and she spoke to her complementary therapist the day before seeing me. They decided that she needed to stop fighting the disease, to accept that she was dying and to have trust in the outcome. 'I could see that I was getting sicker and felt like a failure,' she told me. 'When we looked at why I got cancer, it soon became apparent that I have never really loved myself. I've been a battler and a high achiever, a single mother, a professional and an influential person. I've always been a "doer" and put others before myself. Despite achieving through my life, I always felt that I was failing in some way or another.'

We talked a little about how high achievers are often driven by their fear of failure.

She continued. 'I now need to give in, to surrender and to trust in the divine. I feel so sick, so tired and in so much pain that I'm desperate for relief. That's why I'm turning to you.'

We looked at her symptom control. She had pain in her liver, which was due to secondary cancer, as well as low abdominal pain from partial bowel obstruction. When I examined her I found the cause of this to be a mass of cancer blocking most of her rectum. Once I expressed confidence about improving her symptoms, she started to talk about her faith.

'I had a strict Catholic upbringing, which left me with a lot of fear and guilt. I used to teach the faith in Sunday School but had to reconcile my religious beliefs when I was divorced, and regretted how dogmatic I'd been. Getting cancer has given me food for thought. Like everything else in my life, I've been doing everything because I thought I had to. I've been doing meditation and doing complementary medicine. Frankly, I'm sick of it.

'What I really want is to love myself, to trust and surrender, and to experience God loving me.'

Expanding on her view of God, she told me, 'I'm a bit of a heretic these days but basically still a Catholic. I see God as all that is good within us, and as all that is divine outside of us. If only I could trust in this and surrender enough, I would experience so much love. To me, God is like an ocean, which is probably what has motivated me to live by the sea.' Paula had recently moved to the coast. She said, 'As an ocean, God is vast and unlimited. I have been sitting on the beach, opening myself up, trying to feel God's company and relationship. Despite having faith since childhood I've never felt such closeness as I have now. My "busy"-ness, doing and achieving, have been separating me from experiencing the oneness that is God.'

By talking about her desire for union with the divine, Paula was recognising that the divine is ever-present, and that our own thoughts, words, attitudes and actions connect or separate us from experiencing oneness or union. They can separate us from all the good that is within us, and all that is divine outside us. I sometimes think that we were once the true children of God but have now become separated like orphans.

I believe there to have been times in my life when I experienced divine union with God. The first occasion followed the catharsis I shared in Chapter 4. When we have an experience of union it is both existential and clarifying. It feels like a spiritual window has opened, which, for the first time, enables us to see clearly. However, there is a vast difference between attaining and maintaining such union. We can attain the experience of divine union and realise our eternal identity, yet remain body-conscious. Despite the experience we can still be influenced by negative thoughts or feelings, which keep separating us from the divine. It is by control over the direction of our thoughts that we begin to discover how to maintain our spiritual wellbeing.

In the East there is a saying that our final thoughts lead us to our destination. Gandhi illustrated this as he died at the hands of an assassin, repeating the words '*Rama, Rama*'. His final thoughts were of God (*Rama*). Although the saying relates to the thoughts we have at the time of death, it is also true of life. The mind travels in the direction of its thoughts. Body-conscious thoughts of waste, negativity, worry or arrogance immediately separate us from the divine. On the other hand, soul-conscious thoughts around our true spiritual identity or the virtues of others bring us into union with the divine.

If we could consistently discern truth from falsehood, then we would always think in a fashion that connects us to the divine. Such thoughts embody peace and love as our constant experience and expression. Everything we perceive through the fabric of body-consciousness is deceptive. Even that which is colourful and attractive can separate us from our divinity.

When souls are no longer misled by body-consciousness, they are able to develop and maintain divine union. I saw this exemplified in 1992, while attending an international Raja Yoga meditation retreat organised by the Brahma Kumaris in India. Their spiritual headquarters reside in the rarefied atmosphere of Mt Abu, overlooking the plains and mountain ranges of Rajasthan. The gentle, contented and peaceful expression in the eyes of the resident yogis captivated me. They were surrendered, and they revealed purity in their words and deeds.

The retreat subsequently demonstrated to me that divine union, soul-consciousness and surrender creates an atmosphere full of love and peace. A sensitive soul entering this atmosphere finds within love a quality that is more than an emotion or a feeling; it is also an intelligent energy that seeds within us the truth of spiritual identity. This has led me to think of divine love as love that has the power to reveal truth.

My original encounter with divine union was one of enlightenment following catharsis. In Mt Abu, I discovered that union can also be attained and experienced through meditation. Since then I have adopted the practices and the disciplines of Raja Yoga. Its aim is to attain purity through maintaining union with the divine, which requires effort, awareness, determined thought and discipline.

Divine union purifies in two ways. One is by the direct clearing of negative sanskaras (personality traits) from the soul, while the other involves recognising and realising our original pure sanskaras. It is essentially a process of self-transformation. The sanskaras of negativity affect the soul like rust on a shiny needle. Once corroded, a needle can no longer recognise a magnet or be attracted to it. If cleansed of the rust the needle sparkles and, with its magnetism restored, it leaps to the magnet. Likewise, a soul 'corroded' by body-consciousness neither recognises nor is attracted by the divine. When it becomes enlightened, however, a relationship with the divine can remove the 'rust' and restore the magnetism of purity. Once again, the soul becomes attracted to the divine.

When Paula was describing God, she likened the divine to a vast and unlimited ocean. As souls rediscover the divine, it is as if they are rivers meeting this ocean. By merging into the qualities of the ocean we begin to recognise and realise our own original qualities.

The Ocean of Knowledge invokes our wisdom,
The Ocean of Peace invokes our original nature of peace,
The Ocean of Love invokes our innocence,
The Ocean of Mercy invokes our understanding,
The Ocean of Purity invokes our happiness, and
The Ocean of Forgiveness invokes our freedom.

The divine could be seen in this way, as a vast treasure store of inexhaustible powers and virtues. Through the cleansing of negativity and the invocation of purity, I believe we can become, *once again*, created in the image of the divine. The soul can become pure from impure, soul-conscious from body-conscious, rust-free, sparkling and perfect … just like the divine.

Two specific disciplines involved with attaining and maintaining union are meditation and remembrance. I learnt about these in Mt Abu. On one occasion I had been walking along a track leading from the meditation complex around the mountain to a wide ledge. After sitting on the ledge, I took in the breathtaking vista in which mountains rose from the plains of a desert basin, then ambled their way towards the Pakistan border. With eagles gliding serenely beneath me I had about twenty minutes of meditation.

Rising from the ledge I then followed the track in a full circle back to the Mt Abu complex. The ledge eventually gave way to less spectacular terrain and finally a tarred road, which skirted one side of a lake before entering the lively Mt Abu township. By the time I returned, I had walked from the tranquil mountain, through the bustle of the town and back to the serenity of the complex.

As I entered the complex there was music playing, which I barely noticed at first, and continued walking. All at once my attention was drawn to the stillness and silence within the compound. Everyone had stopped whatever they were doing and had become motionless. They were standing or sitting silently, conversations frozen mid-sentence.

It was 'traffic control'.

Respectfully, I stopped walking, became still and was absorbed into an atmosphere of peace. But there was more than peace. There was something deeper, something greater that I couldn't recognise at first but then understood. It was power. Not the competitive, self-centred power of ego but the benevolent power of spirituality.

This traffic control was conducted for three minutes every two hours, with the aims of maintaining union with the divine

and of staying in remembrance. Everyone makes a simultane-
ous effort to stop the 'traffic' of thoughts and turn the mind
to the divine. The result is pure vibrations of love and peace,
which unify the complex.

One of the yogis explained it to me. She said, 'God is
teaching us here that we are souls. Each one a divine spark
of living energy, a tiny point of spiritual light centred in the
middle of the forehead.' She pointed to the centre of her
forehead and continued. 'We remember this throughout the
day, and we stay connected with God, the Supreme Soul,
through this remembrance. During traffic control we first
clear our minds, then share just the one unifying thought of
being connected with God.' She paused to let me take this in,
then continued. 'This feeling of connection can be achieved in
several ways. I often use a personalised approach to experience
God in the form of a relationship, such as my Mother, Father,
Friend, Companion or Teacher. Whichever one I need at that
moment. On other occasions I remember His qualities of purity, mercy, love or forgiveness, and experience these awakening
in me. And at other times I simply adopt His form.'

'His form?' I prompted.

'Of a point,' she replied. 'In the form of a soul, God is a
point of light, living beyond the material universe. Infinitesi-
mally small, yet, as an ocean of all virtues and powers, God's
nature is universal and accessible to all. It makes Him seem
omnipresent, like He is everywhere and in everything. Yet
His form is only that of a soul, neither male nor female, just
a tiny point of spiritual light.'

'How do you know this?' I asked.

She chuckled, pointed upwards and said, 'He told us,' before gliding happily away.

When I had understood the object of traffic control, I began to experiment with it for myself. I would open myself, surrender, and find the experience of union to be exquisitely simple. It also resulted in me experiencing a relationship with divinity throughout the day. I gradually learnt more of the yogi lifestyle during my time with them. They were making a sincere and disciplined effort to surrender completely to God, while considering this single act to be one of world service. 'The vibrations of peace reach the whole world from a surrendered soul,' I was told.

The day begins at three-thirty in the morning, when they aim to awaken with the thought *I am a child of God*. They then proceed to *amrit vela*, the first meditation of the day. In the meditation of Raja Yoga the aim is to attain a union in which the soul 'remembers' God, the divine Mother and Father. So it is meditation, divine union and remembrance. All three.

My yogi friend explained. 'In Raja Yoga meditation we attain a divine union with the Supreme. We call this the seed stage. The highest stage. It is also a beautiful remembrance of our Spiritual Father, and our World Mother. We remember that we are souls, while receiving love and power from God. Our aim, throughout the day, is to maintain this connection and consciousness. But it is easy to forget, to become absorbed in our responsibilities, actions or work, and to break our link with God. This is why we have traffic control together. It reminds us to stay in remembrance, to stay connected at all times, whatever we are doing. In this way we are surrendering, and becoming instruments of the divine.'

Everything the yogis do is done with the spiritual effort to remain in remembrance throughout the day, whether cooking, cleaning or eating. The early morning meditation leads into a day where, ideally, the yoga-link remains unbroken such that remembrance enters every thought, word and action.

On one occasion my yogi friend explained how they meditate. 'We first of all sit comfortably. We are not concerned with particular postures. Nor do we concentrate on our breathing. Those are aspects of Hatha Yoga. In Raja Yoga we are only concerned with being soul-conscious and having divine union. We meditate with our eyes open because it is better for concentration and because we are learning to stay open-eyed in remembrance throughout the day. Our sitting meditation of the morning leads into our "walking, talking" meditation of the day. In effect, yoga is our way of life, not just what happens when we meditate. We try to maintain our connection with God constantly. To whatever extent we achieve this, to that same extent we are sustained, cleansed and purified.'

'What, exactly, do you do when you meditate or have yoga?' I asked.

'Well, once comfortably seated, with the eyes open, we first explore our thoughts. We check the mind, and gently make it stable. We withdraw our thoughts from the body, the bodily relationships, the world around us and our roles and responsibilities. While doing this we apply a full stop to any wasteful or negative thoughts towards others. Before long we have the single awareness of being a soul, a point of light situated behind the centre of the forehead. Once stable like this, we next "fly" in the vehicle of the mind beyond this corporeal (physical) world, into a relationship with God.'

'You leave the body? I mean, does the soul leave the body in meditation?'

She smiled patiently. 'No. It is the mind that travels beyond the physical body and the material universe. It is the mind that experiences union or yoga with the Supreme. The mind is a faculty of the soul and it flies on the wings of thought, or on the wings of a pure desire. We call this the flying stage.'

'So,' I asked, 'where do you fly to?'

'We remember our home in this stage, where we come from: the soul world or Nirvana. It is the "land" of peace, in a dimension beyond the physical universe. We remember God, the resident of this land, as a most subtle point of loving energy. In this we experience our highest stage of pure silence. And it is here that we experience being in world service.' She paused briefly, then continued. 'The other "destination" of the flying stage is what we call the subtle region, a dimension God has created, between the incorporeal home and the corporeal world. It is a dimension of light and silence, created through purity.'

As she spoke, she seemed to pause between sentences in a hypnotic way that made one peaceful and attentive. 'We call this the realm of angels,' she said. 'It is an in-between place where we rediscover our own angelic qualities. In the subtle region, rather than as a point form, we experience ourselves as subtle light forms, while feeling free and bodiless.'

'And how do you end meditation?' I asked.

'We return to the awareness of our bodies, seated again in the centre of the forehead. But as we do so we maintain a "bodiless stage".'

'How do you mean?' I asked.

'By holding onto the experience of our form of light,' she replied, 'we maintain our feelings of remembrance and divine union after returning to the physical. In remembrance throughout the day, we endeavour to retain the awareness of this subtle form while going about our business.'

'Is that where the traffic control fits in?' I asked, remembering our previous conversation.

'Yes,' she replied. 'Morning meditation establishes divine union with God every day. At traffic control, we keep refreshing the meditation experience. Effectively, we remain meditative and in remembrance all the time. Yet to see us we are just ordinary, going about our business.'

From my experiences with the yogis of Mt Abu, I appreciated the constant attention and effort required to maintain union with the divine. Extrapolating to spiritual growth in general, we need to develop the habit of initially attaining union in morning meditation or prayer. Then, throughout the day, we need to maintain this connection through a practice of remembrance. At first this takes effort and self-discipline but soon becomes natural or 'second nature'.

Remembrance

This exercise represents the single most significant and influential method for self-realisation. On rising in the morning, make your first waking thought one of divinity, such as *I am a child of God* or *I am one with the Universe*. Use whatever it is that makes you feel that you are in a divine relationship. It helps greatly if you spend ten or fifteen minutes before bedtime preparing your mind for these waking thoughts. Remember, the mind 'travels' on the direction of its thoughts.

Next, refresh yourself if necessary with a shower, or tea or coffee. Do whatever it is that suits your preparation for the most valuable time you will spend each day. Then sit for meditation or prayer. Do so in a fixed place each day. By conducting a regular spiritual practice in the same location, you will create a conducive atmosphere for yourself and others.

Enter meditation as you have previously, though try to do so with your eyes open. This habit will better prepare you to maintain the experience throughout the day. During 'traffic control' through the day it can be a little difficult to close your eyes without people noticing! When I was changing from closed to open-eyed meditation, I would begin with the eyes closed, then open them slowly once I was peaceful and relaxed. I would imagine that I was sitting behind the 'windows' of my eyes, just observing the field of vision, without attaching my attention to anything in it. While doing so, I would keep my thoughts on the divine focus of meditation.

Another useful tip is to use a candle in a darkened room. Resting your eyes on the flame, use this as a focal point to develop *concentration*. After a while you will find yourself simply observing the flame, not concentrating on it. The candle flame could also represent the soul as a point of light energy.

Whether or not you find open-eyed meditation suitable, remove your thoughts from all attractions of the body, the world and relationships. Become aware of yourself in the form of spiritual light and connect yourself, through this awareness, to your source of divinity. Use mental imagery, if you like, to invoke spiritual feelings. This can be either literal, such as imagining yourself walking through a forest, or abstract, such as visualising yourself in the company of angels. Alternatively, you could read from an inspirational text before meditating.

As spiritual feelings enter your meditation, let yourself become silently surrendered and *receive* the company of the divine. This is union. Hold on to it, experience it, value it, nurture it and *remember* it.

Stay like this for ten or fifteen minutes: the longer the better. Almost nobody can stop their mind having thoughts that interrupt such union. If the mind wanders, gently guide it back and re-establish the thoughts that created union. Alternatively, you can simply observe distracting thoughts and let them pass by as if projected on a 'screen' in your mind. Experiment for yourself and see what works for you. Sometimes, when there are difficulties, it pays to stop for a few minutes and start again.

Don't get frustrated or feel like you're failing. It defeats the purpose. I would say that ninety-five per cent of my meditating life has been uneventful in terms of amazing experiences, yet eventful in terms of accelerated maturation. There were periods when I experienced nothing then, *in retrospect*, realised the benefit. We live in a 'quick fix' society today, where people are all too quick to say that something doesn't work for them. Meditation or prayer requires patience, gentleness and ... *faith*. These are definitely beneficial.

When you complete your morning meditation, hold onto the experience of divine union as you re-enter the awareness of your body. Have a determined thought to stay in the company of the divine throughout the day. You could do so by being soul-conscious about yourself and others, or by considering the divine to be your friend and companion. Also have several periods of 'traffic control' through the day. You will be amazed at how long two or three minutes seem when you stop. Yet this much time is easy to afford.

14

Spiritual attainments

At the end of 1998, I revisited the Brahma Kumaris in Mt Abu. During my stay I was asked to meet a group of Indian Raja Yoga students from Mysore, which has around five thousand developing yogis. Their regional co-ordinator was a serene image of purity and realisation.

Whenever she interacted, she became light, easy and happy, making others feel the same way. Immediately an interaction finished, she withdrew into herself and became peaceful, creating an atmosphere around her of peace and power. She seemed to move from one state to the other with exquisite simplicity.

I took great pleasure in her company and admired her economy. Whether in thoughts, words or actions, nothing was being wasted. There was no 'small talk', no awkwardness and no barriers. In one moment she was making people happy, in the next she was making them peaceful.

If I caught her eye for a few moments, my mind would empty of thoughts and fill with love and satisfaction. I had the impression that she was so full and contented in herself that her soul had no desire other than simply to *be*. Without desire there was complete acceptance and surrender in her, which appeared to automatically benefit everyone.

The atmosphere around her was similar to that of acceptance in the dying. It was also subtly different. When someone dies in acceptance, it follows a struggle in which everything is stripped away. Soul-consciousness is attained, but usually without self-knowledge. What I observed in the yogi was complete self-control. She was surrendered and serving through her mind, her attitude and her presence. Her purity emanated a power that influenced without effort. In my eyes she was an angel and a world-server. Her spiritual attainments of soul-consciousness had come from the path of realisation, rather than by the force of circumstance. As she is living rather than dying, her potential to influence is substantial.

In this world some stand out on the basis of their attainments. An athlete is visible when he or she is achieving, yet the discipline, effort and sacrifice involved are hidden. It is the expression or performance that makes people stand out in relation to their aims and objectives. Likewise, on the spiritual path it is attainment that makes a soul stand out.

We have already looked at the efforts, discipline and sacrifices required for successful self-transformation and meditation. To the best of my ability, I will now outline the attainments we can aim for on the path of realisation. Each of these can also be thought of as pure states of acceptance.

The state of grace

In Chapter 9, we encountered Margo's realisation that the beauty she sought externally actually came from within. She was very much at peace when she died after my last visit to her home. Several months later I met her daughter, Genaro, who spoke of their special time at the end. 'In the last week she stopped fighting and accepted everything. Everything about her had changed. It was like she just let go of all her fear and surrendered to God. I know it sounds crazy, but being with her then was like being in the presence of God himself.'

'Yes, I felt that too,' I replied. 'I could see the change in her. All the suffering and struggle were finished. She was just being herself.'

'It was more than that,' Genaro continued. 'I really meant it was like being with God. It didn't seem like Mum at all. The only word that fits for me is grace. I read somewhere that grace is experienced when the nature of God manifests itself here on earth. There was nothing in her heart but love, peace and happiness. When she looked at me I felt a current of love that made me forget everything.'

As she spoke I saw tears in her eyes. Not tears of sorrow but tears of beauty and wonder.

'At first I really missed her but she appeared to me one

night, a few weeks after leaving her body. She didn't say a word. She just stood at the end of my bed dressed as a North American Indian, looking young and vital and surrounded in light. She looked at me in the same way as before, removing all my sorrow with the love and grace of her presence. After she left I spent all night feeling warm and happy. I had the thought that I was to tell you of this encounter. I think it is something you are meant to learn.'

Touched by this, I said, 'Thank you. It is about grace, I'm sure of it. It has been on my mind for the last week. It's amazing that you should choose this moment. If you'd come to me when this happened it wouldn't have meant so much. Serendipity really does come into our lives when we walk the spiritual path.'

Looking at Genaro, I asked, 'Have you seen her since then?'

Smiling, Genaro replied, 'No, but I often feel her presence. I don't think I will see her again. I don't feel I need to. I know she is alive and well, a living angel with the grace of God. What more can I ask for?'

'Only one thing,' I replied. 'To become like her yourself.'

Genaro looked at me first with surprise, then with understanding. 'So she has brought us together to teach me something also. For you it is about grace. For me it is to recognise, in her, my own potential.'

This struck a chord in me. 'Yes, and I've just realised something else,' I said. 'Through her grace you had thought of her as special. Instead, you were meant to recognise your own potential.'

There is something here for us all to understand. To think of someone as special is to separate ourselves from our own potential. We should appreciate the beauty of others and live up to it in ourselves.

'So wherever we find grace,' Genaro continued, 'its real purpose is to show us who we truly are. It's an expression not only of God but also of our own potential. It's as if God is trying to show us that we can be like Him.'

The *Oxford Dictionary* defines grace as 'the unmerited favour of God', reflecting a Christian perspective that we are unworthy. But why would God give grace to the unworthy? To me this seems senseless. Yet it would seem equally profane for others to entertain grace as a human potential. They think that it can only come from God. I believe this to be a conditioned attitude of body-consciousness. Margo's example shows us that grace is also plausible in human terms.

When acceptance develops in the terminally ill, it generally does so after yielding to loss. When soul-consciousness develops through spiritual effort, its basis is faith and self-realisation. Grace emerges in the personality, attitude, words or actions under either circumstance. Whether its attainment follows suffering or enlightened effort-making, grace can hardly be considered an 'unmerited favour of God'. Its human potential has something to do with the inner-self.

Nevertheless, grace remains ill-defined. Where does it come from, and how does spiritual endeavour lead to grace? How can a human being be like God? What are the characteristics that enable a human to *be* grace? When I was originally in Mt Abu I asked these questions of my adopted yogi friend and concluded, 'How do we conduct ourselves with grace?'

'Here we talk about *self-sovereignty*,' she replied. 'When grace is to be found in a human being, there will be sovereignty over the senses. Normally our senses have control over us, making us act and react in certain ways. If we see something happen, or hear about something, we easily become angry, sad or excited. We soon start thinking and speaking of what we saw or heard, creating negative or "wasteful" vibrations through our thoughts, words and actions. Such influences make the state of grace elusive.'

I interjected. 'Hear no evil, see no evil and speak no evil.'

She smiled generously. 'Yes, the three wise monkeys is a good tale and relevant to what I was saying.' She thought for a moment. 'But when we think of evil here, we really mean the vices of body-consciousness. The five "evil spirits" are anger, lust, attachment, ego and greed. In body-consciousness, ego takes the support of these vices through the senses. Desire "pulls" us towards sense-gratification and the soul becomes dependent. When we renounce these dependencies and surrender to God, the senses no longer pull us in other directions. The challenge is for us to take control of the senses and to use them for divine service.'

I considered this for a moment and asked, 'So do you just ignore what is happening in the world?'

'Not ignore,' she replied. 'But we detach through knowledge, understanding and faith. We have faith that all is in divine order and that God is now revealing Himself to transform the world. With this knowledge we do not concern ourselves with the problems around us. Instead we accept everything with the understanding that God has the power to change everything. By staying in yoga (meditative union with God) at all times, we fulfil our role of being co-operative with the Supreme. In this hidden and unheralded way, we are helping in God's task of solving the problems of the world.'

I sought further clarification. 'You mentioned seeing, hearing and speaking. How about the other senses?'

'We free ourselves from the desire to touch and the need for physical expressions of intimacy,' she replied. 'We have love for one another, but it is expressed spiritually through co-operation and eye contact. We eat for the livelihood of our body. We enjoy the food but have no greed or attachment to it. We are not repelled by anything, as this is also body-consciousness. Whether it relates to particular odours, behaviour or personalities, nothing repels a graceful nature. Grace is like a rose that remains constantly open, fragrant and beautiful for all to appreciate. It does not withdraw fragrance or colour from someone with a bad nature, and it is up to us whether or not we appreciate it.'

'So grace or self-sovereignty means to have complete control over the senses,' I said.

'Yes, this is the aim. If you like, think of the body as your kingdom and your "self" as the ruler or the sovereign. The senses are your ministers. They should work for you and you should serve through them. They should be co-operative with your directions …'

'But they run amok half of the time,' I interrupted. 'They are forever chasing after one thing or another. If it's not relationships, it's possessions or the desire to see this, experience that and taste the other!'

'Yes. This is what happens in body-consciousness. The ministers of the kingdom run amok.' She laughed. 'Instead of ruling over your senses, you become subservient as they rule over you. In this world today everyone has forgotten who they are, and everyone is ruled by the desire for "sense gratification". Under such circumstances no one can experience or express grace.

'Through yoga we enter into a relationship with God that enables us to progressively "cool" down the senses. Eventually we can relate through them, without being "pulled" by them. When all our satisfaction comes from the divine, we have no dependencies of body-consciousness and therefore no other desires. When there are no desires left for the self, then we are soul-conscious …'

'And full of grace,' I added.

'With self-sovereignty,' she said, 'instead of being influenced by things we see, hear or feel, we learn to appreciate the divinity in everyone. With self-sovereignty, our senses communicate respect and good wishes for all.'

My next statement also expressed my experience of her company. 'And when people come into connection with grace and self-sovereignty, they are inspired to change themselves.'

'Yes,' she agreed, 'which is the most honest form of service in the world today. As *we* attain sovereignty over the senses, *they* in turn co-operate with the divine, to bring peace and harmony into the world. The senses become instruments of the soul. And the soul, in turn, becomes an instrument of God.

'When we have surrendered completely and the instrument is clear, ego-less and free from desire, the flow of grace from the divine is unobstructed.'

Thus the state of grace or self-sovereignty is one of surrender and self-control. Now free from desire, the soul has nothing to lose and nothing to fear. All that remains is love. This is grace.

The *karmateet* stage

Karmateet is a Hindi (Indian) word that means 'karma-free'. The word karma, literally translated, means 'action'. Karma-free means that the soul is no longer burdened by the sanskaras of its past negative actions. These have been settled such that there is no influence of fear or guilt on how we behave. In a sense the soul has been forgiven for, or cleansed of, its past actions. The resulting karmateet stage is one of love, benevolence and service, where every thought and action brings benefit to the world. To grasp this notion we need to first understand the law of karma.

As the law of karma is generally considered an Eastern philosophy, it is often forgotten that it is reflected in Christian teachings. In his letter to the Galatians, Paul wrote: 'For whatsoever a man soweth, that shall he also reap.'[4] The basic premise here is that we will receive the return of our actions and experience life accordingly. Right action is rewarded with good fortune, while suffering is the consequence of wrong actions from the past.

The contentious issue is around the question of rebirth, which is contrary to orthodox Christian teaching. Years ago, in my early days of meditation, I followed a self-training manual called *A Course in Miracles*.[5] This holds that the concept of rebirth is immaterial, as the soul has only one spiritual life. Whether or not the soul adopts different physical forms is of no consequence, as there remains but the one life. *A Course in Miracles* holds that the real spiritual challenge is to develop a divine perception of the world around us, to let go of fear and to return to love.

In Chapter 9 we met Margo in a state of acceptance before she died. When I originally met her she was utterly shocked, angry and confused by her diagnosis of cancer.

'Why me?' she lamented. 'What have I done to deserve this? I've led a good life and taken care of myself. I don't smoke or drink and I care about others. The world is full of bad people who abuse themselves and others. How could God do this to me and let them get off scot-free? It's just not fair!'

As we have seen, Margo moved on from here, but this question of shock and disbelief is very common. Where did the disease come from? Why has it happened? Why now? I sometimes encounter the more complex issue of someone associating his or her situation with a specific past action.

Manifred was admitted to our palliative care unit with

metastatic pancreas cancer. He was in a very terminal state, extremely wasted, dependent and suffering from chronic severe pain. The pain was unusual, however, in that it was non-specific and generalised. It didn't accord with the distribution of the cancer and didn't respond to pain killers. He seemed tormented and I wondered if his pain was related to some form of spiritual despair.

When I explored this, he told me that he was sure he was being punished. During World War II he had a role in which he had to torture prisoners, sometimes to death. Very distraught, he told me with explicit detail some of the more sickening instances. For nearly half an hour he confessed all, then said he was certain that his past actions were related to his cancer. Once the guilt had been expressed, his torment subsided and the pain became manageable. He died within forty-eight hours, but needed to be sedated towards the end to relieve his restlessness.

Whether Manifred's suffering was the result of his wartime activities I cannot say. I do believe, however, that the soul is accountable for its actions. While Manifred was clearly tormented by guilt, I also feel his intuition reflected a hidden awareness of karmic laws. Actions leave sanskaras (subconscious impressions) on the soul. Good actions accumulate benefit for the soul and are returned as good fortune. Such fortune might be realised immediately, as in a reward for generosity, or it might be kept 'in stock' for a future life or 'birth'. Charity in one life, for instance, could lead to wealth in the next. Negative actions that are selfish or cause sorrow also have their karmic returns. These will manifest as some form of suffering, which can also be immediate or delayed. If the return is delayed, then that account is kept in stock within the sanskaras for settlement in a future birth.

It is somewhat like having a karmic 'bank account' within the soul, which is debited by bad actions and credited by good ones. Before coming into physical form, the soul had a clean slate with neither positive nor negative accounts. As I discussed earlier, the soul is deceived by body-consciousness and progressively loses its innocence. As its purity reduces, its accounts accumulate a progressive karmic debt. From time to time the soul's accounts have to be balanced, its sanskaras cleared and its original karmateet (karma-free) stage restored.

Many souls are born with the primary purpose of clearing their karmic accounts. Consequently, many people die while still young. I always look on a child with cancer as an old soul. Having remained innocent from birth, a child develops cancer despite the absence of significant karmic accounts from this lifetime. I remember one child called Jordan because his mother, Lucy, was quite remarkable. She thought of Jordan as a wise old soul who had been sent to teach her.

At two years of age, Jordan developed a neuroblastoma in his pelvis. It had already spread to the liver and bone-marrow. Neuroblastoma is the fourth most common childhood malignancy and affects about ten out of every million children. When it presents in infants less than one year old, it is generally curable. When it develops in older children and has already spread at the time of diagnosis, cure is more elusive. It is a frustrating disease for those who treat cancer because it usually presents with extensive secondaries in the older children. Although it responds well to chemotherapy initially, it may recur and become resistant to treatment.

The cancer specialist told Lucy all of this and summed up: 'About seventy per cent of children respond to chemotherapy and one in five can live for more than three years. Without treatment Jordan will die within a few months.' She decided to go ahead with chemotherapy, which was really the only option.

Lucy told me that the treatment was a nightmare. Over the next six months Jordan went for regular chemotherapy. The treatment was aggressive; it made him very sick and all the hair on his body fell out, even his eyebrows. He required two additional hospital admissions for serious infections brought on by the chemotherapy. Lucy said the whole thing was nearly unbearable for her, and Jordan was terrified every time he went to hospital. Nevertheless, it worked, and Jordan's cancer went into complete remission.

Lucy was overjoyed, and naturally hopeful that he was cured. From that point on, Jordan had to see doctors regularly and was admitted to have scans and other tests every three months. His growth was stunted and normal development was delayed. Otherwise, all went well for nearly three years. Then Lucy was given the terrible news that the cancer had returned and more chemotherapy was needed to keep Jordan alive. 'It won't cure him though,' she was told.

It all started again. The disease in Jordan's body was partially controlled this time. He hated hospitals and doctors, and created a fuss every time his therapy was due. After two months Lucy refused to let them treat him any further, but she agreed to continue with regular check-ups. As Jordan's condition deteriorated she was put under pressure for him to go back on chemotherapy, and was made to feel responsible for him getting worse. Jordan's stomach swelled up with the disease and his ribs fractured. He was put on morphine for pain control, and he became constipated and vomited frequently.

Lucy refused to see the specialist any more. Concerned about Jordan's welfare, the paediatrician contacted me and asked if I could get involved as a palliative care doctor. He expressed particular concern for the child. He believed that Lucy had distanced herself emotionally to the point that she was neglecting Jordan. In fact, the specialist was quite angry.

'I think she is irresponsible,' he told me. 'She doesn't seem to care about Jordan. She seems distant and quite detached from how seriously ill he is. We feel she may be neglecting the child's emotional needs and are concerned about her lack of intimacy.'

I contacted Lucy and she agreed for me to visit Jordan, who was now five. I wasn't sure what to expect or whether I would be able to help. I was particularly concerned about the question of abuse as I had no experience in this. As it turned out, I was pleasantly surprised. There was clearly a close love bond between them, and Lucy seemed committed to Jordan's welfare. Jordan was very unwell, with a huge abdomen, sunken eyes and a frightened face. Lucy smiled apologetically. 'I'm afraid he's seen too many doctors. He's afraid of the things you do to him and afraid that you might put him in hospital.'

Returning her smile I said, 'Don't worry, I'll work things out with you. You know Jordan better than anyone so we'll see what the problems are first. I'll have a talk to him before I go and only examine him if it is absolutely necessary.'

Lucy looked relieved and put on a video for Jordan to watch. He brightened up immediately, realising that I wasn't about to do anything nasty to him.

Lucy and I discussed their experiences in the next room. She was grateful for the opportunity to talk, especially when I agreed that refusing chemotherapy was in Jordan's best interests. By that stage it couldn't cure him and was causing more suffering than his disease. At the end I asked Lucy how she felt about Jordan, his illness and the fact that she would lose him soon.

Although she was only twenty-four, Lucy showed a depth of wisdom that astounded me. 'I'm not worried about him,' she replied. 'I know he is a wise old soul who has come here to settle his accounts and to teach me. I also believe that he will be going on from here to become a great soul. I don't feel I will lose him and I think of us as eternally bound. I only hope it won't take too long and that he won't have to suffer too much.'

'You believe in reincarnation, then,' I said.

'Yes, and I've read a great deal about it in the last three years. Only special souls get sick and die when they are as young as Jordan. They really come to teach us and move on. Having Jordan is the greatest gift I have ever received. A clairvoyant told me at the beginning that he would only be here for a short time. She said I needed to exchange my love for his greater wisdom.'

'Does Jordan know this?' I asked.

She laughed. 'No. I've tried to talk to him about it but he doesn't understand. He's seen other kids with cancer and knows one or two who have died. He believes in life after death and still talks to them sometimes, as if they were in the room with him.' She thought for a moment, then continued. 'He once told me that we go up to heaven when we die, then, when it's our turn, God sends us down to a new life. Where he got that from, I'll never know. My clairvoyant told me that young children still remember where they've come from for a while. She also said that we forget our purpose for coming here, and that Jordan would not understand his spiritual evolution until he leaves his body.'

We talked for some time about spirituality and our reason for being. We had much in common in our philosophy and outlook, so I felt free to express my beliefs without the fear of being intrusive. I assured her that we would not make Jordan go to hospital, and that we would do everything to make his death at home comfortable. Over the next few days we were successful in controlling the pain, constipation and vomiting. Consequently, over the last six weeks of his life Jordan was comfortable and relatively happy. I became his favourite doctor because I left him alone! Towards the end he went into a coma due to kidney failure and died very peacefully.

One other interesting thing happened. After my first interview with Lucy, I rang the paediatrician to reassure him of Jordan's welfare. I told him about Lucy's way of seeing things and that I felt she was close and loving towards the child. Her apparent distancing, I thought, reflected her spiritual awareness. This included her acceptance of Jordan's death. I said that I thought she was a good mother and I didn't think that Jordan was being neglected.

In response, the paediatrician was angry. He clearly thought that I was an eccentric and that Jordan now needed his supervision. He said it was imperative that he see Jordan on a regular basis. I contacted Lucy diplomatically and told her that the specialist would still like to see Jordan. But the relationship had broken down long before — perhaps when she felt forced to accept further chemotherapy — and Lucy did not go back with Jordan.

In regard to the law of karma, I believe that Jordan was clearing past accounts in this birth. A disease of such complexity can only emerge in an experienced soul. When a new soul takes its first birth, its slate is clean with no sanskaras capable of manifesting disease in childhood. To develop childhood cancer, to be born with a deformity, or to be 'developmentally delayed' all require the experience and accounts of past births, so these are always old souls. Observing children with cancer is one of the influences that has convinced me of the existence of past lives.

When I was involved with Jordan, Lucy asked a question I hear frequently.

'Dr Cole, how can you do this sort of work? Don't you find it sad and depressing? It must be hard for you, knowing that you can't change anything.'

It is a question I have given a considerable amount of thought to. My reply began like this. 'With people like yourself and Jordan there is a sense that nothing more can be done. In fact, you often feel deserted when medical treatment has failed. Our approach in palliative care is different. We understand that much can be done to control pain and suffering. We also understand how important it is to have support at times like this. We love to see the difference this makes, so our work is very rewarding.'

The second part of my reply had to do with spirituality. 'The other thing that keeps me happy in this work is my outlook on life. I have recognised my own eternal identity, so I see this in others also. Suffering is just a temporary period of adjustment for the soul. I don't really witness the suffering; I observe it and offer comfort. What I see is a soul beginning to realise its full potential through clearing the karmic accounts of past births. In this way I can remain detached from the suffering, yet be close and loving in the relationship. Instead of worrying about my patients I send them love. I figure that love has more value than worry.'

I don't see suffering as a 'just desert' or look on it as a form of punishment. I see it as a natural process that cleanses and purifies the soul. I think of it as concealed growth in which past karma is being settled at a personal level through illness. The soul is being set free, and benefit will ultimately come. This may happen in the absence of spiritual awareness, yet it is a spiritual process.

Apart from the karma of illnesses, we may also develop specific group or relationship karma. As a consequence of the past we find ourselves in relationships with people we have accounts with. We have no knowledge of our past-life encounters and find ourselves settling accounts by serving those souls suffering in a relationship or causing someone pain.

Group settlement might take the form of an accident or a calamity, such as a plane crash or an earthquake. According to the law of karma there are no accidents, coincidences or luck. Whatever happens in life has been determined by past actions, and relationships have already been established.

It is not essential that a soul suffers to settle its past accounts, though this can't always be avoided. When the soul is enlightened it engages the path of realisation and its growth is revealed. Within suffering, spiritual growth is concealed, whereas within enlightenment, it is apparent to the self and others. When we come into a relationship with the divine we can directly clear our accounts and old sanskaras. We also learn how to serve humanity through our nature and attitudes. On the basis of human service, spiritual relationship and divine union, we can also move along to our karmateet stage. To whatever extent we succeed in these three, we limit our potential for suffering.

Once at the karmateet stage, the soul sees the world with

deep love, understanding and detachment. It is then a divine image, beyond fear, doubt or desire. This stage is the end of our cycle from purity, through body-consciousness and back to purity. At the outset we are innocent yet vulnerable to a world we haven't experienced. At the end we are innocent yet knowledgeable of a world we understand.

Being complete with all powers

As we become soul-conscious we progressively develop self-respect based on spiritual awareness. This enables us to see the world differently, through a divine vision of brotherhood and sisterhood. In the East, such spiritual awakening and perceptual clarity is referred to as the 'third eye' opening. When conditioned by body-consciousness, the spiritual knowledge, virtues and powers of the soul become latent. Though present, they are hidden and obscured from expression. When we meditate and make spiritual effort, we gradually draw on this latency, and these qualities resurface.

Raja Yoga meditation teaches that soul-consciousness is attained through self-knowledge, divine union, pure expression and human service. Once complete with all powers, knowledge and virtues, the soul is said to be in its highest stage. We have already entertained knowledge of our eternal identity throughout this book. We have also seen how to develop our virtues, and how to discern these in others. We will now consider how to awaken and utilise eight specific powers of the mind.

The eight powers

The eight powers enable us to control and focus the flow of our thoughts and actions. Through clarity, consistency and integrity, they make us trustworthy and influential without being forceful or controlling. They give us the ability to recognise truth, to succeed in our spiritual objectives and to uphold our spiritual identity in a body-conscious world. In the first instance we apply them to break the habits and conditioning of body-consciousness. Later, when we have become soul-conscious, they simply form part of a loving and virtuous nature.

I will first outline the application of spiritual powers to growth and transformation, then describe their natural expression when we are soul-conscious.

The *power to withdraw* enables us to become introverted where situations might otherwise have influenced or affected us. This power was part of the yogi's 'economy' described on page 123. Withdrawing into herself she could disengage, centre herself in truth and make the atmosphere peaceful. It is particularly important to practise withdrawing so that it becomes easy to achieve even when there is disturbance around you. When someone starts to gossip, criticise or get angry, withdraw into your awareness of being a soul. Instead of becoming involved in something wasteful, become introverted and simply observe it like a scene in a drama. This habit makes you less vulnerable and preserves your peace of mind. You also reduce the risk of spreading someone else's negativity.

The *power to pack up* means to apply a full stop in the

mind. Instead of thinking or worrying about people or situations, we develop the power to complete a task or interaction and then pack up our thoughts. Once it has passed, we don't waste our energy wondering about the consequences. This enables us to always give our full attention and energy to the present moment. By stopping us from worrying about problems, the power to pack up is a form of mind control that prevents negative expansion from occurring. Such expansion can make little problems seem big, leading to complexity, anxiety and stress. When we apply a full stop, we are able to see a big problem more clearly and it becomes small.

The *power to face* means to have courage and a capacity to change. While cultivating our inner beauty we must also recognise, acknowledge and free ourselves from weaknesses. Just as we need courage to face the challenges of our external world, we need courage to face weaknesses inherent to our body-conscious nature and conditioning. When we are challenged or criticised this is an opportunity to see our weaknesses, if we have enough self-respect and honesty. Don't be hurt but look to see if there is the slightest justification.

- Has someone seen something that I can change?
- Was I a little forceful?
- Did I really give my full attention to their position?
- Is there still some arrogance within me?
- Was I lacking in tolerance?

After checking yourself you can resolve to change some aspect. In this way those who seem to be 'obstacles' in our lives actually challenge us to become stronger and grow spiritually.

With the *power to tolerate* we maintain equanimity while constantly giving regard to others. This enables us to remain easy and make others relaxed. True tolerance does not mean putting up with someone while harbouring feelings of dislike towards them. Rather, tolerance relies on love and understanding, in which we maintain good wishes even for those who try to hurt or defame us. We can understand why people misbehave when we realise that wrong action comes from body-consciousness. When you tolerate in this way there is an automatic feeling of forgiveness. You don't even begin to be judgemental, so remain unaffected by wrong attitudes, words and actions. True tolerance is a disposition of love towards a world of conflict and illusion.

The *power to accommodate* means to make room in the heart for everyone. Whether or not we agree, there is respect for different views or opinions and only love is returned to those with a negative or irritating disposition. As an ocean merges a raindrop, so too the power to accommodate enables us to merge difficult situations and conflicts within the self. When something unexpected happens you remain unaffected, as the power to accommodate fortifies your capacity to love.

The *power to discriminate* is a discerning intellect, which recognises spiritual values and acts accordingly. The more we pay attention to this, the more spiritually accurate we become. When giving, distinguish which thoughts, words or actions will impart peace or happiness, and elect never to cause sorrow. When receiving, take nothing from others that would cause unhappiness or make you body-conscious. If someone offered you a piece of rotting fruit, you wouldn't take it except to be polite and accommodating. You certainly wouldn't eat it. So if someone speaks to you with anger, jealousy or greed, listen if you must but don't digest what is said or take it away with you. If someone tries to influence you with dishonesty, turn away. If someone tries to spoil your view of another person, do not enter into it. Look for and accept only virtues from others. In the spiritual effort of appreciation (Chapter 9), we determined to always look beyond weaknesses and seek good qualities within others. This was about using the power of discrimination to receive spiritually. You attain this power when you can distinguish virtues and leave 'rubbish' behind.

The *power of judgement* makes us accurate in decision-making and action. Clearly, this requires a discerning intellect and the power of discrimination. Once you have discerned with spiritual accuracy you then use judgement about your action. It is possible to discriminate effectively, yet misjudge the reactions of others. You may act with the best of intentions, yet offend or impose on someone. Don't think they lack gratitude but face the fact that your judgement might have been weak. To develop the power of judgement, check the results of words or actions against the question, 'Was there benefit, or did someone suffer?' And that question should include you.

With the *power to co-operate* we make the task of world benefit easy. We use this power to spread spiritual feelings and values, which is a means of co-operating with the divine. When you give trust to others you increase their self-confidence, and when you communicate your motives you make them feel part of a whole. When you give co-operation in this way, you will receive it from everyone. Your power of co-operation thereby influences the spread of spiritual attitudes.

~

So the eight spiritual powers taught in Raja Yoga are to withdraw, to pack up, to face, to tolerate, to accommodate, to discriminate, to judge and to co-operate. When they are working in unison with spiritual knowledge and virtues, the soul becomes complete and attains purity. Such a soul is stable, mature and gentle. It is compassionate and giving, and remains constantly at peace with itself. Unattached, yet responsive and loving, it combines the perfect balance of firmness and flexibility while *accommodating* any situation with love. Centred in truth, a pure soul exercises wisdom, courage and cleanliness as it *withdraws* from any disturbance of waste or negativity. It is understanding and benevolent, while treating everyone with respect and humility. Such a soul remains unaffected as it deals with problems, then *packs up*. By never going into negative expansion the soul remains light and contented, warm and accessible. It is fearless, with the power *to face* any of life's challenges. This soul recognises its own value and *co-operates* with the service of human enlightenment. While co-operating it *discriminates* accurately, and only gives co-operation to that which brings benefit. Surrendered and free, a pure soul has clear *judgement*, and expresses natural authority with no need for force. Obedient to the directions of the divine, such a soul is rich and forgiving in its capacity to *tolerate*.

On the path of realisation we ultimately attain all powers and become free from body-consciousness. With meditation we identify the eight powers, then use them to break body-consciousness, and to serve others. As soul-consciousness emerges, we express the powers effortlessly with only our virtues visible. With this effort, in time, the soul returns to love and is an image of love.

Being a world server

All spiritual and religious teachings include human service as an essential component of expression and development. Spiritual growth along the path of realisation is no exception. We can serve through *what we do* for others and through *who we are*. During my life as a palliative care physician I have come to realise that *what we do* is a limited form of service. It is the service of *who we are* that can be truly far-reaching. If we are soul-conscious while serving others, then the quality of our attention or care is greatly enhanced. If we practise remembrance to sustain ourselves, then we emanate peace through this expression of faith. If we are contented while conducting mundane tasks, then we influence those who witness our happiness. These are aspects of natural, effortless service that come from one's attitude and perspective.

In Chapter 4, I discussed my encounter with latent spiritual possibilities following a post-cathartic experience of love.

Encounters like this are 'spiritual windows' that offer a glimpse of our full potential and bring new insights and enthusiasm for the journey. My second 'window' experience occurred in 1992, on a mountain summit in India during a sunrise meditation. I had an experience of unity, in which all boundaries between myself and others became artificial. There was very little sense of my own identity. It seemed as if I had dissolved and become part of all that *is*. At the same time I felt at one with God. It was as if my soul, the divine and everything else were in union. For twenty minutes in that early morning light I feel that I became an instrument of love. Through meditation I had stepped out of the way and allowed God to reach my soul and work through me.

I discovered later that this was what they describe in Raja Yoga as the 'seed' stage of meditation. It is a state of divine union in which one becomes 'bodiless', and an instrument for world service. With magical simplicity the soul becomes a pure, unobstructed channel for spiritual love, which seeks out the sensitive, awakens the ready and enlightens the worthy. Such world service is both unique and unlimited. Unique because it extends directly from the divine, through an individual to the world. Unlimited because there is no need for proximity or contact. World service contrasts with the limitations of more familiar worldly service, where we rush around in our work roles or engage in charitable work. Such service is limited by our body-consciousness. While compassionate support for one another is essential, the service of divine union and surrender has a 'far-reaching' quality.

About a year after my trip to Mt Abu I received confirmation of this, following a similar meditation experience at my home. On that occasion I sat and developed the awareness of being a soul, a subtle point of divine light. From this point, in the centre of my forehead, I connected with the divine nature, personality and purity of God. As I felt the 'current' of this union, I again experienced the seed stage. I had a particular awareness of divine love passing through me to everyone I had been connected with, past and present. As I left the meditation I had the clear feeling that service had been done. I was also aware that we can settle our karmic accounts through meditation. These accounts keep us bound to relationships with certain souls who receive love and power through our meditation.

Later that same day, Fran came to my office saying that she needed to speak to me. I had known Fran for years as an oncology and palliative care nurse. She'd had some back problems and I had supported her application for a job that didn't require heavy lifting. Fran had a dream the night before and felt compelled to tell me about it.

'I was climbing a mountain without ropes or assistance. As I was nearing the top I became tired and reached an overhang. It was very dangerous but I had no choice but to proceed, as going back was impossible. Anyway, I started to climb the overhang but I was very tired and got stuck with a sheer drop below me. I was terrified. At that moment, just before I fell, you appeared beside me and helped me over the last part.'

Fran seemed slightly embarrassed. 'But it wasn't really to do with you. I woke up knowing that it was really to do with God. The dream reassured me that there is nothing to fear in the future. I know help will always be there whatever obstacles I face. It has given me confidence.'

I sat in wonder, feeling that she had been 'sent' to validate my meditation experience. I told her about my morning meditation and how I thought it was related to her dream and realisation.

'What time was it when you woke up?' I asked.

'Just before four-thirty,' she replied, which was during my meditation.

There are two things that especially touched me. The first was Fran's awareness that her support came from God, even though I was the figure in the dream. This fits well with the idea that we become instruments of the divine as we surrender and 'allow' God. Second, Fran hadn't been in my mind during meditation, yet had an experience through our connection. It taught me that if we remove the blocks from our minds, we can realise an unlimited potential to serve from afar. Once sceptical of the 'absent healing' conducted by some prayer and meditation groups, I now had to accept its validity.

It is possible to become a constant world server when we are experienced in meditation. With the capacity to withdraw at will, we can adopt the 'bodiless' seed-stage in a natural, easy way without appearing to meditate. Our original virtues and powers emerge and every thought carries purity and goodwill to the world. Absent healing is the very nature of one who has the spiritual attainment of a world server.

The angelic stage

Ralph was 'ordinary': a 63-year-old carpenter who had lung cancer. I met him ten days before his death, following his admission to the hospice. He was distressed with pain, breathless and very frightened. He didn't really understand what was happening but knew that people with cancer died in our establishment. I spent some time with him, reviewing his recent history and checking his chest X-ray. Apart from being breathless, he didn't look too bad and I didn't think his death was imminent.

I told him this. 'Ralph, the cancer is quite advanced on your X-ray and it is making you short of breath. But, comparing it with an X-ray from two months ago, it hasn't been growing too fast. I just think that it's got to a stage where it's making you breathless. I really don't think you are dying at the present moment.'

I noticed that he was calmer and was giving me his full attention. I could see he was eager to be informed and wanted to know why things were changing. I talked to him about cancer and showed him the X-rays to help him understand.

'What we need to do now is to control the pain and breathlessness with small, regular doses of morphine. I think you will be much more comfortable by later this afternoon.'

We spoke for a while longer about the treatment. Towards

the end I asked him, 'Is there anything that you're particularly afraid of at the moment?'

He replied, 'Yes, I'm terrified that I will suffocate and choke to death.'

This is an extremely common fear of anyone who has experienced breathlessness with lung cancer.

I consoled him in this way, 'At the moment I believe you will improve. If, by any chance, things were to get worse, then we would offer you sedation. We don't allow people to die struggling for breath here. We would keep you asleep so you wouldn't be aware of any feelings in your body.'

He looked relieved and squeezed my arm as I left. Now that he was informed, he felt reassured and trusting of his care-givers. When I returned a week later he was no longer breathless, was pain-free and was now quite calm. However, he was also much weaker and it was evident that he would die soon. We talked about the increasing weakness and I asked him how he felt about it.

'I don't think there's much hope, is there?' he replied.

'How do you mean: not much hope?' I asked, to which he said, 'Well, I'm not going to get better, am I?'

We went on to discuss his prognosis and the fact that he wouldn't live very much longer. He wasn't distressed at all by the frankness of our talk. In fact, he was relieved to know what was going to happen and appreciated my openness. He said that living had become a struggle and he was happy that he didn't have to fight any more. On my final visit he looked peaceful and was sleeping. I wouldn't have disturbed him but he opened his eyes as I was turning to leave. Clear, blue and contented, they contrasted with the frightened, furtive eyes of just over a week ago.

Sitting up, he smiled at me as I asked him how he was feeling. The answer was quite surprising and disarming.

'I feel like I'm blessing everyone.'

As he said this, I found myself experiencing a profound sense of peace in his presence.

'After you spoke to me that first time, I was so much easier on the inside,' he continued. 'I knew what was going on and why I was deteriorating. It took all my fear away. I was never frightened of dying, actually, but I was afraid of pain and suffering. You don't know what it meant to discover that I wouldn't choke to death.'

After a moment he said, 'On the second occasion you confirmed what I already knew — that I was dying. It felt wonderful afterwards and I just let go of everything. I stopped fighting and struggling. In fact, I have been feeling better than I can ever remember. I've been completely at peace just lying here. I can hardly describe what it's like. I'm ready to die but in no hurry to do so. As long as I feel like this, I'm happy to be around.'

'Have a go at telling me what it feels like,' I suggested.

'As I said,' he continued thoughtfully, 'I feel like I'm blessing everyone. I'm incredibly light, almost floating. And it feels like I'm surrounded in light, as if there is a huge cocoon or halo all around me. At times I can even see it. I lie here feeling like I'm rising from my body and just keep observing light all around me. There are even moments when I feel that I'm a part of it.'

While he was speaking, I found myself experiencing the things he was describing and suddenly realised that he truly was blessing everyone. We seemed somehow connected, and when there was eye contact it felt nothing like the company of a mortal being.

Ralph carried on. 'Although I'm lying here, I don't feel limited to my body. If I think of anyone, past or present, it feels like I'm instantly with that person and that my company is a blessing. Although I'm definitely in this body, it seems as if my mind can be extended beyond it. And it feels as if I'm travelling in the light that I was describing.' He paused, searching. 'There is one other thing that I can identify. There is nothing but love, inside and out. It seems that I have become love.'

Ralph was tired by the effort of talking and needed to rest again. As I left, I glanced back from the doorway. His eyes were half-open, gazing into the distance. He looked beautiful. I couldn't see the light that he had described but I could feel it. Ralph continued to deteriorate but he remained peaceful and didn't need the sedation we had discussed. He really did leave his body the next day and everyone remarked how they had felt blessed by him. On admission to the hospice, Ralph was an ordinary, frightened man with cancer. By the time he left he was almost an 'angel'.

I learnt something of the angelic stage of spiritual attainment from Ralph. He taught me that it is a state of mind. He also helped me to understand the subtle nature of the soul and its capacity to extend itself through the vehicle of the mind. When I was in Mt Abu, an experienced yogi described to me an ethereal realm she called the *subtle region*. She said it was an intermediate dimension of purity and light between the 'soul world' and the corporeal physical world. It is a 'place' where we are able to experience our subtle light-form, as well as our 'angelic' nature, which is pure, carefree and light in character. Ralph reflected this before leaving his body. He seemed to be free of his body and its limitations, while still in it.

Meditation also teaches us to become 'bodiless' while still in the body. By bodiless I mean that there is no remaining trace of body-consciousness. As with Ralph and other examples of acceptance, the mind is no longer drawn to superficial concerns and is free from desire. When there is such purity, the mind can enter the subtle region at will. One may then reach others through thoughts, while experiencing the presence of light. It is generally more accurate to say that this 'light' is experienced rather than seen, although there are sensitive souls who seem able to witness it. Examples include those people who can see auras, and others with the psychic capacity to see apparitions.

In Chapter 7, I described Tegan, a child who entered my consultation room twelve months after she had 'died'. There is no question in my mind that I encountered her ethereal (light) form. I also believe that when Ralph was experiencing light, he was actually sensing his own ethereal body. The same, I feel, is true of others who see light during altered states of consciousness, such as in meditation, near-death experiences or being under the influence of drugs. We all have an ethereal body, a subtle form in which the soul separates from the physical at 'death'. This subtle form is not in itself an angel. Whether or not it is angelic is determined by the quality of its consciousness.

When Ralph was dying he experienced liberation and lightness, with the sense that he was unlimited and able to bless everybody. The real 'blessing' that he gave was knowledge, as he seeded spiritual awareness in others. When Tegan entered my consultation room her presence created an atmosphere of light, love and healing. In effect, those in the room received a 'blessing' of her company, and experienced the living truth of her spirit.

When Ralph was dying I said he was almost an angel. Although he experienced his subtle light form and had the freedom of a liberated mind, he was lacking in the power of realisation. His nature seemed angelic but the attainment was circumstantial and dependent on dying. As an attainment of human potential, the angel emerges from deep self-realisation and connection with the divine. By awakening to this potential before he died, I feel that Ralph *now* has the prospect of its full attainment and expression.

In Raja Yoga the angelic stage is considered the ultimate aim and object of meditation. Those who attain it can, at will, alternate with the seed stage discussed in the last section. The seed stage is a powerful transforming union in which all sense of personal involvement is lost, as the soul becomes a channel for divine energy. The angelic stage is a more engaging union, where the soul becomes like God. One maintains a sense of self, while expressing divinity through spiritual knowledge, powers and virtues. With the angelic stage a soul attracts to itself but acts in the image of the divine. Surrendered and free from ego, it inspires others to seek and express their own angelic qualities.

The angelic stage is a likeness to God, revealed through those who have the courage to grow. Those who make effort to transform themselves will progressively attain this. Their sign is that they remain constantly carefree, light and beyond the limited concerns of this world. On account of purity they are welcomed everywhere as gentle and virtuous, giving courage and hope to souls 'lost' in a body-conscious world.

Such is the angelic stage of attainment.

Through truth, simplicity, awareness and realisation it is a human potential.

15

Mission of love

Elisabeth Kübler-Ross stated that there are only three types of people in the world today who are honest: children, the dying and psychotics. The latter was a particularly interesting observation from a psychiatrist. In fact, psychotic states are conditions I sometimes see in my work, and view with interest. I think that those who are psychotic sometimes encounter their spiritual potential in a totally unbalanced way. We refer to this as having delusions of grandeur. While out of touch with this world during a florid mental illness, they have no capacity to lie, and relate only what they are feeling.

Early in my career as a palliative care physician I developed a close relationship with a young man who died of AIDS. Damon Courtenay's story has since been published in the book *April Fool's Day*, written by his father, Bryce Courtenay.[6]

When we first met, Damon was twenty-two and had already suffered in his life. He was born with haemophilia, a bleeding disorder caused by the deficiency of one clotting factor. Damon was frequently hospitalised for intravenous injections of the missing factor. One feature of the condition is spontaneous bleeding into joints. Apart from acute painful episodes, Damon developed crippling deformities in his joints, which affected his mobility. He walked with a limp and couldn't remember a day in his life that he hadn't suffered pain.

The timing of his illness was crucial to the following events. It was during the 1980s, just before AIDS became apparent to the Western world. The clotting factors given to Damon had been unwittingly taken from AIDS-infected blood donors. When AIDS was discovered, and Damon was tested, he was found to be HIV-positive. Damon was one of those people who come through hardship with great character development. He was endearing, sharp and mischievous, with a totally positive outlook on life. He and his carer, Celeste, warmed to me when I determined that his chronic diarrhoea was unrelated to AIDS but had been induced by his pain-killers. Not only were we able to get rid of this long-standing problem but we also achieved better pain control than he had experienced before.

Despite a 'roller-coaster' of problems over the next two years, Damon always had a smile and a new 'money-making scheme' when I saw him. Although he had significant periods of doubt and depression, I never saw him dejected and he never lost his love for life.

He enjoyed talking to me about spiritual matters. A gift from his childhood was something that his father had taught him. 'Whenever things are difficult,' his father had said, 'there is a place you can go to. A place that is always safe, and one where you are protected. It is a small, quiet place within you. Go there whenever you need to escape, or when you need to concentrate on something.' Damon learnt to access this place inside, and used it frequently throughout his childhood. What his father had inadvertently taught him was how to meditate and how to be soul-conscious. This gift, I believe, would become the most valuable lesson of his relatively short life. He wasn't actually aware of it as enlightened; it was simply a natural practice. He could 'go beyond' his body and the ravages of disease at will.

During the progression of AIDS, Damon had a psychotic episode where he temporarily lost his sanity. One of the neuropsychiatric manifestations of AIDS is mania. This is a condition characterised by delusions of grandeur, paranoia and 'speedy' irrational thoughts and actions. Over a six-week period he became progressively more paranoid and irra-tional, convinced that the CIA was after him. It culminated in a hospital admission to an AIDS unit that was poorly equipped to manage psychiatric illnesses. Damon suddenly became totally irrational and ran away from the hospital, terrified that *they* were coming to get him. A terrible scene followed in the family home.

Because he was considered insane he was scheduled (de-clared insane), and the police were sent after him. Despite his frail, weak and wasted condition, they forcibly arrested him in front of his shocked family and carers. Damon was taken, screaming and terrified, to a psychiatric hospital, where he had to be forcibly detained and medicated. This was in the early days of AIDS, when there was a huge amount of fear and misinformation about its mode of transmission. He was initially treated like a leper, though this subsequently worked in his favour, as he was assigned a house in the grounds with his own nurses. I went to see him a day after his admission.

The house was an old, musty weatherboard place with pleasant gardens. It was completely surrounded by a high fence, with a double-locked gate. I was shown to the facility by an orderly, who unlocked a huge padlock and removed the chain to let me in. As I walked towards the house, the chain rattled behind me as I was padlocked in with Damon and his 'keepers'. Damon was waiting for me on the veranda. On recognising me, he waved and gave me a huge smile; evidently he was very, very happy.

Far from being a prisoner, Damon greeted me like a lord of the manor, and proceeded to show me around his new kingdom. He introduced me to all the nurses on a first-name basis, telling me that they were his servants! He had no memory of his florid paranoia of the previous day, and none whatsoever of the traumatic events surrounding his detention. He told me that his AIDS had been cured by electromagnetic emissions from a small copper bracelet on his wrist. He said that very soon the whole world would be free from AIDS and all other diseases. As he, Damon, had discovered the secret of eternal life, he was now very important indeed. Consequently, he had been given new headquarters in the hospital, and had been put in charge. The government would soon remove all the patients from the hospital to make room for his operation, which would change the world.

These were the essential themes that Damon related to me. He was excited and spoke quickly, going off on numerous tangents. This creates what we term a 'word salad' of linked but dissociated themes. I have picked the main characters from the 'salad' to express where he was mainly 'coming from'. One of his tangents was a salad created on the word eternal. 'I know God has put me here for this purpose. He wants everyone to live forever. He has given me a mission. Yes, it's a mission, a mission of love. This is why I'm here. The only thing the world needs now, now that I can heal everyone, is to love. This is why the government has made me the boss around here. Eternal life means nothing without love. Giving people eternal life was only the first part; now I have to make them love. I'm a man on a mission.'

Damon was beaming with satisfaction. He was euphoric and absolutely intoxicated with his 'insights'. He was also floridly manic and psychotic. Some months later, when he'd finally recovered from his manic condition, he would confide in Celeste that he missed the certainty, the sense of invincibility, of his own strength in mind and body that the mania had given him. As Damon grew increasingly frail and incapable in the last year of his life, he would sometimes say wistfully, 'It was so great, babe! It was the first time in my life I felt completely whole! I *was* the mighty Damon. If only I could be well and have that same feeling again.'

Despite his deterioration, he maintained his mission of love. In an excerpt from his diary, which was published in *April Fool's Day* two years after he died, he said this:

… Can I tap into a force within my mind to beat the odds, to survive? Love is the most powerful force of all. It is an energy, it is a power. I must use it constructively. I must *stop* listening to the negative forces in my head that tell me that it is beginning to end. I want to give so much to this world, to the people I love.

Then, a little later he said this:

… How to start? The first thing is to have faith in myself again. To take control. To get my brain working again. To live my life around a structured existence. Now I must read, I must write, I must contribute to the person that is me … I must learn to live again.

He concluded with the following words:

… anything can be done if the will is strong enough. It is truly time to explore the spiritual nature of the person that is me. I use that word to describe that which is more than the heart, the bowel, the knee joint. That which makes us more than merely flesh and blood. For that is where the answer to healing and to thriving and to existence and to life is to be found.

I believe that when he was dying in Celeste's arms, Damon found himself to *be* that small, quiet 'place within' that his father had shown him. I think he discovered in that place the secret of eternal life. For that place was himself, with all the illusions removed. And it was his mission realised, for that place was love. I feel the soul that was Damon has moved on to serve the world, and that his mission of love now has the wisdom of a short and full life.

In the last chapter we looked at expressions of soul-consciousness. These are states of attainment, in which one's eternal identity is realised and emerged, such that its purity and grace is visible to the world. They are also states in which the soul has the power to extend its consciousness beyond the physical body and states in which the soul can act as a channel for love from the divine. Damon said that 'eternal life means nothing without love', and he stated that he was now on 'a mission of love'. To seek the spiritual path, to make effort to draw upon the perfection of that small, quiet 'place within', to find God, and to extend this aware-ness as a merciful unifying compassion for all life: this is the mission of love.

16

The power of love

After we enter this world our innocence is progressively conditioned by body-consciousness. As the soul becomes body-conscious, it depends on vices to protect itself and to satisfy its desires. Acceptance of death reveals how a soul can rediscover its original nature of peace. Cathartic and near-death experiences show how enlightenment can lead to the path of realisation. Spiritual effort demonstrates that we can free ourselves from body-consciousness and rediscover our purity. Spiritual growth, then, is a paradoxical journey of 'remembering' who we were. As a journey to love, it can be summarised thus: *As I was, then so I shall become.*

In the midst of mania, Damon Courtenay told me that he was on a mission of love. He later wrote that love, as 'the most powerful force of all', must be used constructively. One of the mistakes of body-consciousness is that we seek love on the outside, when really it lies within. We try to use love and direct love, rather than become it. Our principal mistake is that we mix love with attachment until, fettered with need and dependency, it becomes conditional. We withhold it from those who misbehave, and feel unhappy or angry when it isn't reciprocated. On the one hand, we seek to direct and determine who is worthy of love, while on the other, we find we cannot trust it.

The love that lies latent within is that of our original soul-conscious nature. It is both pure and unconditional. Only when we are soul-conscious can we encounter what it is like to love unconditionally. This may happen before death, during enlightenment, following a catharsis or through spiritual practices. What you experience is simply that you become love itself. You are indivisible from it and so full and complete in its experience that you have no other desires. When I experienced unconditional love following a catharsis, it wasn't love for anybody or anything in my life. I simply was it. If I had said at the time, 'I am love', this would have accurately described my feeling of identity during the experience.

What I discovered about unconditional love is that it cannot be directed or controlled. You can be it but you can't give it. The moment you direct it to one person or withhold it from another, you have placed a condition on it. Ego and attachment intervene as you decide where it should go. As you become soul-conscious, unconditional love emanates from your original personality. The giving of love accords with its own nature rather than your direction. There is no need to help it in any way, for love has its own power. To love unconditionally we must detach from everything else and become love, then let love 'decide'.

A mission can be either a vocation or a place for spiritual service. For Damon Courtenay it was a vocation to bring insights of love and healing to the world. Those who countenance spirituality will entertain the vocation of serving humanity through love. However, because it is easy to mix ego with good intention, it is useful to consider it to be a vocation of love. We should ask ourselves: *What would love do?* This helps us to be humble and to have the humility to let go and let love. If one becomes love, there is nothing to prove, for love is apparent and instantly recognisable. No force is required as love itself can accomplish its own task.

When someone is dying in acceptance they let go of everything and become love. Those who encounter such people recognise this and comment on its beauty. In Chapter 5, June told me that her experience with her dying mother had left her with a firm belief in eternal life. It was, she said, as if her mother became a 'mirror', reflecting truth to all who visited her. A number of the yogis I encountered in Mt Abu had this capacity in life. Their presence could give such an experience of love that all that remained was spiritual conviction. My own experience of post-cathartic love changed me from an atheist to a theist, and led me to a spiritual path.

Love's vocation reveals who we are, transforms body-conscious attitudes and illuminates the path of realisation. Its power is to unify and heal the world. On a mission of love our task is to become love, then to allow *it* the freedom to accomplish its own purpose.

Healing through love

In India the term for religion is dharma, which literally translated means 'way of life' or 'original way of being'. Religion as a way of life is what we call spirituality in the West. True religion, I feel, is the inculcation and expression of all the virtues. It aims not to convert but rather to enable others to experience and express their personal truth. No spiritual path is absolute, though I believe the divine to be an external guiding influence that serves all religions. This service is through the power of love, which has within it unlimited healing potential.

Unconditional love is divine spiritual love. Not only is it latent within but it also resides externally in the divine. If we encounter it externally, the power of love reveals that which is latent within. If we encounter it internally, then love expands until we are indivisible from the divine.

Whatever we experience in life, whatever traumas we encounter and whatever defences we erect, love lies beyond that. However we have changed, however we have been hurt, love awaits our awakening to heal us of the past and free us in the present. At a meditation workshop a few years ago, Monica, a teacher, took me aside to speak to me of a past trauma. When she was a child, her father molested her for a number of years, extending into her adolescence. She thought that she had dealt with its traumatic effects until one of her students confided that she too had been through sexual abuse. In trying to help the student through bitterness, remorse and guilt, she found her own pain resurfacing.

She was angry and bitter that she couldn't confront her father, who had since died. She was also angry with her mother, who had been weak and ineffectual after she discovered the abuse. So disturbing were the memories that they were affecting her marriage and capacity to work. She was also struggling with the dilemma of whether or not to confront her now frail and aged mother. After developing panic attacks and insomnia, she had recently consulted a psychotherapist. Monica said that she felt the experience had left her soul filthy and eternally tainted. She asked me what I thought.

After acknowledging her pain, I talked to her about the soul, of its original purity and how it is conditioned by what we experience. When we are traumatised we find ways of repressing our pain. We lay protective layers like onion rings around the soul, and learn to express ourselves in ways that keep us from being vulnerable. We can hide the pain until we don't feel it, but still it resides within and can reawaken. I said that deeper than this, beneath all the defences and all the sorrow, lies our original purity and innocence. It has been suppressed and it too can reawaken.

'Nothing that ever touches you can harm this,' I said. 'It is impossible for the soul to be eternally blighted through traumas or life-experience.' I went on to say that I hoped she would experience this deepest part of herself during the weekend workshop. I felt that it would then be unnecessary for her to confront her elderly mother about things that had happened so long ago.

Monica wrote to me after the weekend. On the afternoon of the second day she had an experience of profound love and healing, which brought a sense of cleanliness and release. In reflecting upon her experience, she said it felt like a complete purification through the power of love. Recognising this love, she let go of her traumatic childhood, forgave her father and felt no need to discuss it with her mother.

On my second visit to India in 1998, I went to Mt Abu with the aim of discovering how to realise this power of love consistently. At dawn on the fourth day I left the main group and walked to a nearby valley for meditation. The setting was one of perfect beauty, solitude and a silence enriched by morning birdsong. As I meditated I held a conversation with God in my mind. I said, 'I renounce all my attachments to this world and surrender to you alone. I let go of my body, my relationships, my physical wealth and possessions, and even the sense of who I am.' I finished by repeating over and over, 'I surrender to you alone.' As I did so, I experienced myself becoming a direct child of God, which gave me a deep feeling of belonging. By being His or Her child, I also had the feeling of God belonging to me, leading to an experience of love that I can only describe as purity and power. Neither a feeling nor an emotion, it was an intelligent life-transforming energy.

Like Monica, I experienced the power of love as a purifying energy. We can experience its healing qualities under many circumstances, while living or dying. I believe its source to be the divine, and that it awakens when we surrender and 'belong'. I feel that love gives us the power of realisation and makes us like the divine. More accurately, I believe that pure love reaches us to reawaken the image of God that 'sleeps' within us. I think that it would please God if we were to become like Him or Her. I believe this is how we return the love of the divine.

Merciful vision

The power of love is experienced when we become receptive to it through right thoughts, right words and right actions. Beyond this, to extend the healing power of love to the world, we must have no tension or conflict with anything in it. Merciful vision is an attitude that eliminates all division and unifies one's capacity for love with others.

The plea of Jesus at the crucifixion — 'Forgive them, Father, for they know not what they do' — is a simple yet complete expression of mercy. Body-consciousness is the 'blindfold' that separates us from love and truth. Under its influence, fear and mistrust distort perception until the soul no longer acts according to its virtues. Spiritual insight makes us aware that this is the basis for human weakness. Within this knowledge lies understanding, acceptance and forgiveness.

Imagine that a small child comes into your lounge room,

leans on an expensive vase and accidentally smashes it on the floor. The child doesn't know what a vase is, and has no sense of its value. As the child had no idea that the vase could move, let alone fall over, you would consider them blameless and innocent. Even though there is loss, you would not have to forgive because you understand that the child lacks knowledge and experience.

Likewise, people who have become body-conscious have 'forgotten' truth. As they act without knowledge or experience of the soul, they separate themselves from love. Merciful vision is an attitude of true forgiveness, which accepts everyone as blameless and innocent. It allows love and its mission to propagate and spread through society. To develop merciful vision requires faith in our immortality, trust in the divine and acceptance of the unfolding drama. We must also have a lot of love for our human family. Rather than seeing our differences in gender, race, attitudes and behaviour, we can develop a unifying sense of brotherhood or sisterhood. By considering all souls to be children of God, we develop the feeling of a family where everyone belongs to one another. In soul-consciousness we realise the power of love through belonging to the divine. Merciful vision brings a sense of our belonging to the world, which connects this power of love to all other souls.

In the teachings of Raja Yoga there is a slogan, 'When we change, the world changes', which reflects two things. First, as we become soul-conscious, we see and experience the world differently, so the world changes for us. Second, we begin to co-operate with love's task of revealing truth, creating unity and healing the world. As we play our part, as we co-operate with love, our merciful vision is more than a way of seeing the world, it is a way of allowing love into it.

17

The cycle of realisation

As we 'grow' and realise our original nature of peace, purity and power, we embody love. In this return to love, we complete a cycle from soul-consciousness to body-consciousness and back again. Realisation, I believe, is part of the life cycle of every human soul. We fall from grace but our hidden purity cannot be subdued forever. We are responsible for our actions and have to settle our accounts, but love is latent and ultimately irrepressible.

I believe in birth, death and rebirth, and feel that life is a drama in which all souls play a part on the world stage. New souls enter this drama, while old souls continue to be reborn into a growing civilisation. When we fall from grace, so too does our growing civilisation, and its values come to reflect the increasing body-consciousness. Realisation in the individual often follows a crisis, which challenges or destroys the facades of body-consciousness. In its broadest application to humanity, cyclical realisation might see a crisis reached wherein civilisations rise and fall, self-destruct and renew. If this is true, then we could expect a scene in 'the drama' where the world transforms in the midst of chaos.

I received one such warning in 1987 from Vincent, a terminally ill AIDS patient. At thirty-seven he had suffered from the illness for two years and had advanced Kaposi's sarcoma, a malignant condition characterised by purple patches growing in the skin. By the time I met Vincent, this had also spread to his liver, lungs and spleen. He had been in the hospice for three weeks when he asked me to pay him a special visit. As he had no medical or psychiatric disturbance of the mind, what he had to say was intriguing.

He told me that he had been having visions of the future. In these he saw two main features that foretold of impending cataclysm. On one side he saw a nuclear world war, causing mass destruction of human life. On the other, a series of natural disasters culminating in huge earthquakes, tidal waves and flooding. He said these events would occur soon after the turn of the century. 'The first sign,' he said, 'is a tyrant, worse than Hitler, who would emerge from the East.'

He said that the events all had spiritual significance and that these were 'biblical times'. Armageddon, he told me, was not the clash of good and evil depicted in the Old Testament. It was a 'nuclear cleansing' for humankind. Likewise, the apocalyptic scenes of natural disasters were to prepare the world for revelation, and the coming of a new age. In these final scenes of his vision he saw a legion of angels bringing love, unity and healing to the world in its darkest hour.

Vincent said, 'Dr Cole, I haven't told anyone else of these things.' Pointing upwards he said, 'I was "instructed" to tell you because, in time, you would understand. I guess you'll probably think I'm crazy.' I thanked Vincent and assured him that I didn't think of him as crazy, although I was more of a sceptic in those days.

Despite his vision, Vincent didn't have a particularly peaceful death. He had been depressed before the hospice admission and struggled within himself, right up to dying three weeks after our discussion. He never spoke to me again of visions; in fact, he became quite distanced, withdrawn and troubled. At the end he became breathless and agitated with pneumonia but was able to die comfortably under sedation.

Vincent's predictions accord with those of other visionaries and psychic commentators for this millennium. Best known is Nostradamus, a naturopath and astrologer of the Renaissance period whose credibility and fame stem from the accuracy of his predictions, especially of events in the last 100 years. The problem with prophecy, however, is that it only becomes objective after the fact and is viewed with scepticism. This in turn makes it unpreventable! So prophecy has major limitations, and is not particularly useful to the wider community as a learning or education tool.

Though sceptical, I didn't discard Vincent's warnings as I had been having similar, albeit less visionary meditation experiences. The encounter with Vincent occurred three years after I was enlightened by Kübler-Ross. It was over these years that I began to meditate on the divine nature and form of God. Instead of trying to reach the divine on my terms, I had recently discovered the experience to be easier when I simply 'allowed' God. There was no need for force. The divine is ever-present and all we need to do is to become open and accessible. By surrendering and 'allowing' God, I was learning to subjugate my ego to God's will. As a result, I began to experience a loving divine union, which included a compassionate feeling for humanity. I also began to receive impressions, not visions, of the times we live in. What I experienced in meditation was a wave of spirituality and truth emerging against a background of social decay. I sensed a divine community being established amid scenes in which chaos, conflict and desperation preceded a global realisation and peace. There was, concurrently, world renewal and destruction of body-consciousness.

If realisation and world renewal were cyclical phenomena, then an enticing possibility exists where prophecy could come from a 'memory' or sanskara within the soul. Having lived this age repeatedly, could Nostradamus, perhaps, have 'remembered' the future? If realisation is a cyclical phenomenon, we might expect to find cultural evidence for cyclical time. We might also expect to find evidence that technologically advanced civilisations have previously existed. Furthermore, if this is the age of realisation, it should be evident now that humanity is capable of self-destruction.

In *Wisdom of the Elders*, acclaimed scientist, author and environmentalist David Suzuki contrasts Western science with the diametrically opposed traditions of 'age-old wisdom' from indigenous people around the world.[7] Written with Peter Knudtson, the book explores the delicate relationship between humans, nature and the environment. Their research took accounts from surviving cultures within developed countries (American Indians, Australian Aboriginal people), as well as from third world communities.

They write that in contrast to the Western worldview, in which time is linear and arrow-like, native societies traditionally embrace manifestations of circular time, 'sanctifying them with their rituals and awe'. Looking at the universe through the Western worldview, Suzuki and Knudtson say, one is fortunate to grasp even a transient sense of the spiritual rhythm and cycles of nature. Through the native perspective of cyclical time, nature is absorbed into a timeless dimension that is both spiritually and ecologically charged. The indigenous people of the world have respect for the land, its flora and fauna. They also have knowledge that to interfere with the cycles of nature is to invite destruction. Familiar patterns of the past — great cycles of growth and decline, birth and death, ecological devastation and renewal — can, and perhaps will, re-emerge.

Cyclical time appears in the traditional stories of the Navajo Indian people, who describe long-term expansions and contractions of the universe. They conceive that the world first stretches outward from the centre then springs back, culminating in a perfectly symmetrical, pulsating movement over the whole period. Cyclical time is also revealed in the creation stories of their ancestral holy people. These relate that the first people emerged from sacred openings to the core of the nurturing earth. They then dispersed across the land in all directions. In the great mythic cycle, the souls of deceased Navajo continuously return, and join with newborn souls to grant order to the natural world.

Many Navajo now believe that humankind is living quite precariously. The attitude of white people has destroyed the sacred and natural rhythms of nature, and a crucial time is coming when the Earth and all its inhabitants will experience *another* period of cataclysmic collapse.

Such is also the widespread view of many different native people from around the planet. The difference between these beliefs and the prophecies we discussed earlier is that they are based on mythology rather than psychic phenomena. There is evidence that mythology has a sound factual base, handed down in story-form through successive generations.

Graham Hancock explores this in his compelling book, *Fingerprints of the Gods*.[8] He compiles evidence that past civilisations existed that were both sophisticated and more technologically advanced than we are today. In a journey through Central and South America and the Middle East, he catalogues and details the unexplained mysteries of these regions. He also identifies common threads in the mythological beliefs of ancient, now extinct, people who were geographically and culturally distinct.

Mythologies from both the Middle East and the Americas have a 'Noah's Ark' scenario cast in images of cataclysm, destruction and flooding, followed by widespread community disorder. In the Americas, 'civilisers' are then depicted to have come into those communities, bringing order and high-living values. Pictures, carvings and statues depict these as bearded Caucasians in white robes, despite the fact that the communities they entered were of non-Caucasian background. They were also depicted as leaving again by sea in an age when we were, supposedly, unable to navigate, let alone have the technology to travel across the Atlantic.

Hancock concluded that the whole developed world was flooded at an apocalyptic time of massive earthquakes and volcanic activity, that the society of the time was both sophisticated and technologically advanced and that the cataclysm wiped out most of the population. The existence of common themes, within culturally distinct groups, suggests that there is a factual basis to what is generally considered myth. It also appears that those communities recorded, and handed down, their stories to successive generations. That 'Noah's Ark' occurred in the Middle East and the Americas suggests that a common experience founded these stories.

He gives further evidence for flooding and a raised sea level in the establishment of Lake Titicaca as a seaport community with elaborate farming and irrigation techniques. Lake Titicaca is now 3820 metres above sea level! Building techniques used in Machu Pichu in Peru, as well as the pyramids in Egypt and Mexico, still defy explanation. Huge stones with smoothly cut surfaces that we cannot yet replicate are aligned with pristine accuracy. There are only a handful of cranes capable of lifting these today and none that could have aligned them at their locations. Apart from size and alignment, the mathematical technology used for the planning processes is only now emerging with modern computing techniques.

A fascinating mystery surrounds the cartography, or mapping, of our oceans. The land mass of Antarctica is accurately outlined on maps dating back as far as AD 1513 (the Piri Reis Map, made at Constantinople). Yet it is known that this coastline had been covered in ice for thousands of years before that. The technology to identify a land mass under the ice was only developed in the latter half of the twentieth century, and it has confirmed that maps drawn centuries ago were accurate. Thus, as it is known that the Antarctic coastline couldn't have been drawn in our recorded history, Hancock concludes that it must have been copied and handed down from originals drawn thousands of years ago. He also concludes that advanced technology must have been available at that time. He states that, as cartography is an activity of sophisticated communities, they must have been both civilised and well developed.

There is evidence, therefore, that advanced civilisations may have existed in the past, with access to some technologies we can't yet match. We now have the nuclear capacity to destroy our current civilisation. We have almost denuded the planet's natural forests, have created a hole in the ozone layer and appear unable to control our greenhouse gas emissions. Consequently, the world's weather patterns are changing, on the one hand with droughts and crop failures, on the other with massive flooding and other extremes. It seems to me that humankind has developed a huge karmic debt with the planet that is being settled by nature itself.

In considering these possibilities, I would like to convey the possibility of a spiritual renewal emerging in a time of entropy and chaos. Whatever upheavals you may witness in the world, uphold your eternal identity and allow the power of love to support souls during increasing difficulties. In the potentially difficult times ahead, let any disturbing scene invoke your spiritual efforts to bring peace to the world. Instead of getting caught up in the events, let yourself become of service through your spiritual knowledge, love and understanding.

18

The ashram of your life

I was seated on my suitcase in Ahmadabad airport, on my return journey from India in 1992. There was nowhere else to sit. The domestic departure lounge was chaotic, my flight to Delhi being one of several that had been delayed. A group of angry Indian businessmen were shouting and gesticulating at the baggage handlers. Despite the disturbance, and despite being tightly scheduled for a connecting flight in Delhi, I felt blissfully detached and serene. *Sweet drama!* I thought, and smiled inwardly. *At least I have a seat.*

I was enjoying a sensation of perfect inner peace, upheld against upheaval and chaos. I was not worried about making my connection in Delhi. I just observed everything without desire, concern or anxiety. I felt wonderfully free and liberated.

Any doubts that had gone through my mind during the

meditation retreat in Mt Abu were dispelled. At that moment it seemed as if they were dispelled forever. In fact, they had dispersed in the afterglow of a magnificent sunset meditation. High in the mountains, the divine had 'spoken' to me in a 'voice' that was still echoing through my mind.

At the end of the meditation retreat I had nothing planned for the following week. I had heard from visiting Western Raja Yogis that a special meeting was to take place, a meeting of mystical union in which the divine communicates and gives directions for the soul and for world renewal. I was urged to stay but there were a few things I didn't know about. Those who could attend this meeting were allowed to be there on the basis of their spiritual effort, self-knowledge and surrender. They also had to have followed certain disciplines of purity for a number of months.

To stay on I needed permission from Dadi Janki, a head administrator of the organisation. Physically short in stature, she had disarming power in her spirituality. She engaged me with a sensitive challenge to my spiritual commitment. If I accepted this knowledge, surrendered myself and adopted the disciplines of pure living, I could stay. If not, they would be unable to accommodate me. I was to go away and think about this, then return to see her again in a couple of days.

I had expected to know clearly, one way or the other, what to do. As it turned out, I was left with considerably more uncertainty than I had before meeting her. No longer was it just about staying; it now had another unexpected dimension. Was I spiritual enough? My feelings fluctuated between indignation and self-doubt over the next few days. *If such an opportunity exists, how can one person deny another such a meeting?* I pondered. Beneath this was a nagging feeling of being unworthy.

Nevertheless, I felt attracted to the communal life of these yogis. I was drawn towards surrendering myself and living the 'monastic' lifestyle of the ashram. (Ashram is an Eastern term that describes a spiritual community following common principles and teachings.) So further confusion compounded my doubts and uncertainty: *Should I leave my life for this? Will I find God in this place? Do I surrender and stay here? Is this attraction part of the divine plan for me?*

The answers came, not through a meeting the following week, but later that very same day on Baba's Rock, Mt Abu's favourite place for sunset meditations. As the sun disappeared that evening, my awareness was beyond all its beauty. There were no physical sensations, as my body, the earth and the universe seemed to stand still. It felt like I was in a time warp, filled with divine insight, and unaware, temporarily, of my own existence.

I cannot say that it was an experience of love; this would follow. Nor can I say that it was an experience of peace; this also would follow. What I can say is this: it was an experience of clarity and of divine presence, and of a voice speaking in the deepest, most ancient part of my soul. Its words of wisdom and direction finished all my confusion about divine meetings and finding God. It said, *It is not by living in an ashram that you will find Me. But it is through the ashram of your life that you will know Me.*

The message was a dual one of example and service. As you develop and experience the reality of your spiritual beliefs, they become a power in your life and lead to the natural expression of inner beauty, wisdom and strength. Observe without judgement, and you will reveal love. Speak without arrogance, and you will teach love. Act without complexity, and you will become love. When you become love, you belong to the divine and your life becomes the ashram.

It also becomes a mission.

19

Simplicity

The habits of body-consciousness make spiritual growth and attainment seem esoteric, elaborate and challenging. Yet the original nature of the soul was one of great simplicity. Complexity arises when body-consciousness conditions the soul, with its dependencies, desires and uncertainties. It is actually body-consciousness, rather than spiritual attainment and realisation, that is complex. What we are seeking is simplicity and truth.

If you exclude the body, what remains is thought energy, an organising intellect and memories (including sanskaras). We are all the same whatever our gender, beliefs or cultural background. If we leave the current life we do so as this conscious living energy. In transforming body-consciousness and realising our true nature, we are becoming sensible. We can look at the same world and be deceived through body-conscious eyes, yet understand it accurately when we are soul-conscious.

Raja Yoga teaches that consciousness emanates from a point of light, which is the form of the soul. Although the form never changes its simplicity, purity and power do. In Raja Yoga, God is considered to be the only soul who never enters the cycle of birth and death. Without gender, He or She never becomes body-conscious and never loses His or Her purity and power. With such simplicity, the Supreme Soul never seeks to direct or control love and never becomes attached to anything. As God remains eternally in His or Her original nature, He or She never stops being love and never stops allowing love. In time, all souls can rediscover their original peace, purity and power through this One who never changes.

When we are body-conscious, the soul seems esoteric, yet it is our true identity. We substitute the new reality of that which we deem objective, measurable, concrete. We turn away from truth and instead embrace the temporary illusion of body-consciousness. The mysterious, the unexplainable or the miraculous amaze us, yet these are ordinary expressions of our original nature. Soul-consciousness heals us of ignorance and deception, yet we think of this as enlightenment. To grow back to who we were, to return to love, we need to understand that soul-consciousness is our most ordinary, uncomplicated way of being.

With soul-conscious simplicity we are easy, open and honest. In simplicity, truth is visible and realised with nothing to prove. Through it we experience the depth of our own truth, become economical with our lives and benevolent with our love.

~

There is nothing elaborate about soul-consciousness. As you journey through these paradoxes, your influence will grow as you become more ordinary. There is no need to change anyone but yourself. Love will do the rest.

Have a good life and a good journey.
Be simple, be you.
Be sensible, be true.
Om shanti.

Notes

1 Elisabeth Kübler-Ross, *On Death and Dying*, Touchstone Books, New York, 1997.

2 J. M. Small, 'Sixth Sense', *Lancet*, Vol. 337, 1991, p. 1550.

3 Sogyal Rinpoche, *The Tibetan Book of Living and Dying*, Harper-Collins Publishers, New York, 1994.

4 The Bible, Galatians 6 : 7.

5 *A Course in Miracles*, Foundation of Inner Peace, Viking Penguin, New York, 1996.

6 Bryce Courtenay, *April Fool's Day*, Penguin, Melbourne, 1998.

7 David Suzuki and Peter Knudtson, *Wisdom of the Elders: Sacred Native Stories of Nature*, Stoddart, Toronto, 1992.

8 Graham Hancock, *Fingerprints of the Gods: The Evidence of Earth's Lost Civilization*, Crown, New York, 1995.

About the Brahma Kumaris

The Brahma Kumaris World Spiritual University is an international organisation that teaches Raja Yoga meditation as a free community service. It is affiliated with the United Nations as a non-government organisation with consultative status in the Economic and Social Council, and with consultative status in UNICEF.

Should you wish to look further into the meditation philosophy discussed here, I have listed the contact numbers of the main centres in Australia. From these contacts you can obtain the details of centres or contacts near you, and determine whether there are courses available in your area if you live at some distance from the main centres. All teaching is voluntary and most centres run a free introductory course in meditation. As these contact details are subject to change or if you live in other parts of the world, you may prefer to access the Brahma Kumaris Internet sites at www.bkwsu.org or www.bkwsu.org/au for a current listing of international contact numbers, or more information about the organisation.

Brahma Kumaris main centres

Australian Capital Territory
Canberra   (02) 6260 5525

New South Wales
Ashfield (Sydney)   (02) 9716 7066
Leura, Blue Mountains Retreat   (02) 4784 2500
Newcastle (02) 4957 2223
Wilton Retreat Centre   (02) 4630 8124
Wollongong   (02) 4227 2241

Queensland
Gold Coast (07) 5575 2126
Brisbane   (07) 3368 2391

South Australia
Adelaide   (08) 8338 4531

Tasmania
Hobart   (03) 6278 3788

Victoria
Baxter (Retreat Centre)   (03) 5971 1599
Essendon (03) 9374 1112
Fitzroy   (03) 9417 4883

McKinnon (Melbourne)   (03) 9578 9955

North Balwyn (Melbourne)   (03) 9857 8871

Western Australia

Perth   (08) 9388 6101

Other books by Dr Roger Cole available at

www.eternityink.com.au